FAVORITES

Number 3

A Collection of Gospel Songs

for

SOLO, DUET, TRIO, QUARTET

and

GROUP SINGING

Compiled by

ALFRED B. SMITH

Singspiration® Inc.

WORLD DISTRIBUTORS

ZONDERVAN PUBLISHING HOUSE

GRAND RAPIDS, MICHIGAN

The response to the first two volumes of "Favorites" has been continued and ever increasing. For this we are indeed thankful. To us it is evidence that their contents are truly "Favorites."

Favorites No. 3 is a worthy addition to the Singspiration series. On its pages will be found only songs which have proven themselves by continued use.

"Sing"cerely yours,

Alfred B. Smith

1 HARBORED IN JESUS

Fay Wallingford — Don M. Allen

1. Once I was drift - ing, lost and in sin, Once I was dy - ing, darkness with - in. Now I am liv - ing the way He planned. Har-bored in Je - sus, Kept by His hand.
2. Storms may sur-round me, tem-pests may roar, Doubts may as - sail me, knock at my door. Noth - ing shall move me from Je - sus' side. Har-bored in Je - sus, Won-der - ful Guide.
3. In joy or sor - row, bless-ing or pain, Tri - al or test - ing, His peace re - mains. Trust - ing Him whol - ly, heed - ing His call, Har-bored in Je - sus, my all in all.
4. Friend, are you drift - ing, with none to care? Friend, are you dy - ing, deep in de - spair? Come un - to Je - sus, He'll set you free; Har-bored in Je - sus, e - ter - nal - ly.
Chorus
Harbored in Je - sus, safe and se - cure. Har-bored in Je - sus, safe ev - er - more.

I HAVE FOUND A HIDING PLACE

Chas. F. Weigle — Gladys Blanchard Muller

1. I have found a hid-ing-place when sore dis-trest, Je-sus, Rock of
2. I have found the sweet-est flow'r that ev-er grew, Je-sus, "Rose of
3. I have found a love-ly star that shines on high, Je-sus, "Bright and

A-ges, strong and true; In a wea-ry land I in His shad-ow rest,
Shar-on" fair and pure; He's my joy and com-fort, bless-ed Friend so true,
Morn-ing Star" to me; In the night of sor-row He is ev-er nigh,

He is my strength in all that I do.
He blooms with-in my heart ev-er-more.
He drives the dark-est shad-ows a-way.

CHORUS

Je-sus, "Rock of A-ges," let me hide in Thee; Je-sus, "Rose of Sharon," sweet Thou art to me; "Lil-y of the Valley," "Bright and Morning Star," Fai[illegible] to my soul.

3 I'VE DISCOVERED THE WAY OF GLADNESS

F W H

Floyd W. Hawkins

INTRO.

Solo

1. Man-kind is search-ing ev-'ry day In quest of some-thing new; But
2. I've found the Pearl of great-est price, "E - ter-nal life" so fair; 'Twas

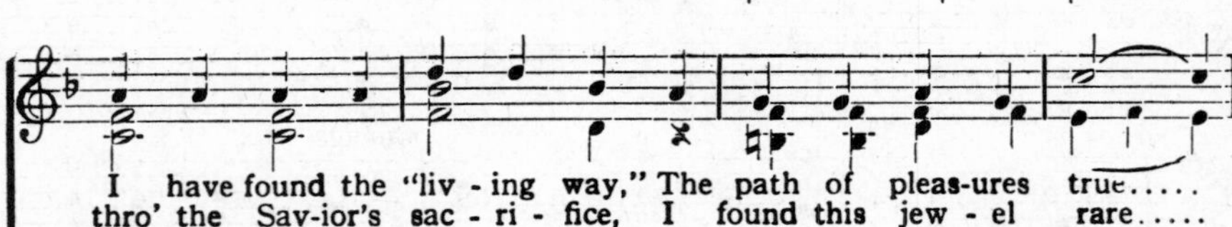
I have found the "liv - ing way," The path of pleas-ures true.....
thro' the Sav-ior's sac - ri - fice, I found this jew - el rare.....

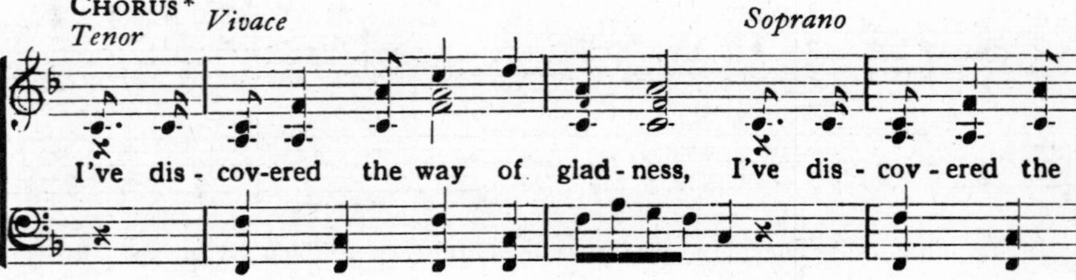
CHORUS*
Tenor
Vivace
Soprano
I've dis - cov-ered the way of glad-ness, I've dis - cov - ered the

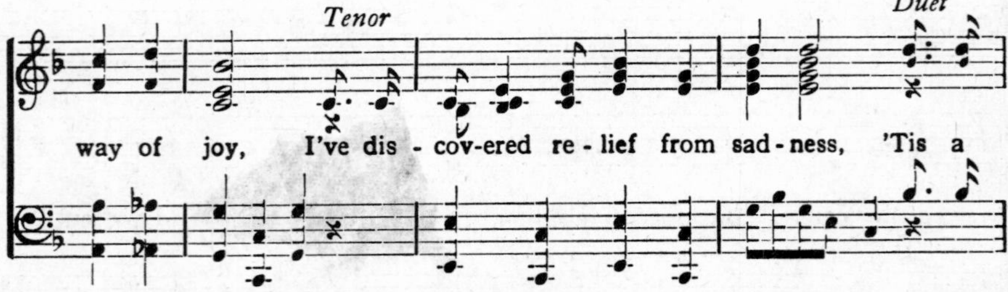
Tenor
Duet
way of joy, I've dis - cov-ered re - lief from sad-ness, 'Tis a

I'VE DISCOVERED THE WAY OF GLADNESS

Tenor
hap-pi - ness with-out al - loy; I've dis - cov-ered the fount of
Soprano
Duet
bless - ing, I've dis - cov-ered the "Liv - ing Word," 'Twas the
great-est of all dis - cov - er - ies When I found Je - sus, my Lord.
4
WHERE COULD I GO?
J. B. C.
Copyright, 1940, by Stamps-Baxter Co. in "Golden Key"
J. B. COATS
1. Liv - ing be-low in this old sin-ful world, Hard-ly a com-fort can af-ford;
2. Neighbors are kind, I love them ev-'ry one, We get a-long in sweet ac-cord;
3. Life here is grand with friends I love so dear, Com-fort I get from God's own word;
Cho. Where could I go, O where could I go; Seek-ing a ref-uge for my soul?
D. C. for Chorus
Striv-ing a-lone to face temp-ta-tions sore,
But when my soul needs manna from a - bove, Where could I go but to the Lord?
Yet when I face the chill-ing hand of death,

Need - ing a friend to help me in the end, Where could I go but to the Lord?

JESUS IS ALWAYS THERE

B. M. L. — Bertha Mae Lillenas

1. Some-times our skies are cloud-y and drear-y, Some-times our hearts are bur-dened with care; But we may know, what-e'er may be-fall us,
2. When in the midst of life with its prob-lems, Bent with our toil and bur-dens we bear; Won-der-ful thought and deep con-so-la-tion:
3. When we are walk-ing thru the green pastures, Or o-ver moun-tains rug-ged and bare; Pre-cious the thought and sweet the as-sur-ance,
4. "Lo, I am with you al-way," is writ-ten, God will not fail to an-swer our prayer; Trust-ing His word we rest in His prom-ise,—
Je-sus is al-ways there.
CHORUS
Nev-er a bur-den that He doth not car-ry, Nev-er a sor-row that He doth not share; Wheth-er the days may be sun-ny or drear-y, Je-sus is al-ways there.

HOW CAN I HELP BUT SING

Sheldon G. Helsley
Helen Griggs
SOLO
1. Once a stran-ger far from God and home, I wan-dered thru this
2. Can it be that there has come to me Such joy I hard-ly
3. Some glad day, per-haps not far a-way, He'll take me to His
world of sin; But Je-sus heard my cry, He would not
can con-tain! My life is filled with song each day and
home a-bove; Where, face to face, I'll see this One who
pass me by, I whis-pered, "Lord," He took me in!
all night long,—His blood has cleansed a-way each stain.
died for me And praise Him for His match-less love.
CHORUS
How can I help but sing Since I've found a Friend in Je-sus;
Al-ways my praise shall ring . . . Since I've found a Friend in Him.

7 THE MERCIES OF GOD

T. O. Chisholm
Jesse B. Thomas

1. The mer-cies of God! what a theme for my song, Oh! I nev-er could
2. They greet me at morn when I wak-en from sleep, And they glad-den my
3. His an-gels of mer-cy en-com-pass me 'round, Where-so-ev-er my
4. His good-ness and mer-cy will fol-low me still, E-ven on to the
num-ber them o'er; They're more than the stars in the heav-en-ly dome,
heart at the noon; They fol-low me on in-to shades of the night,
path-way may lead; Each turn of the road some new to-ken re-veals—
end of the way; I have His sure prom-ise and that can-not fail,
Or the sands of the wave-beat-en shore.
When the day with its la-bor is done.
Oh! for me life is bless-ed in-deed.
That His mer-cy en-dur-eth for aye.
CHORUS
For mer-cies so great, what re-
turn can I make? For mer-cies so con-stant and sure? I'll love Him, I'll
serve Him with all that I have As long as my life shall en-dure.

BALM IN GILEAD

(*Medium Voice*)

Old Traditional
Arr. by Herman Voss

INTRODUCTION
There is a Balm in Gil - e - ad To make the wound-ed whole;
There is a Balm in Gil - e - ad To heal a sin - sick soul.
1. Some - times you feel dis - cour - aged, And you think your work's in vain,
2. If you can - not preach like Pe - ter, If you can - not pray like Paul,
And then the Ho - ly Spir - it Re - vives your soul a - gain.
You can tell the love of Je - sus, And say, "He died for all."
CHORUS
There is a Balm in Gil - e - ad To heal the sin - sick soul.

9 I WON'T HAVE TO CROSS JORDAN ALONE

Thomas Ramsey — Chas. E. Durham

1. When I come to the riv-er at end-ing of day, When the last winds of
2. Of-ten-times I'm for-sak-en, and wea-ry and sad, When it seems that my
3. Tho' the bil-lows of sor-row and trouble may sweep Christ the Sav-iour will
1. When the last
sor-row have blown; There'll be some-bod-y wait-ing to show me the way,
friends have all gone; There is one tho't that cheers me and makes my heart glad,
care for His own; Till the end of the jour-ney, my soul He will keep,
winds of sor-row have blown;
I won't have to cross Jor-dan a-lone.
Chorus
I won't have to cross Jor-dan a-
I won't have to cross
lone. . . . Je-sus died for my sins to a-tone; When the
Jor-dan a-lone,
Solo ad lib.
Parts
dark-ness I see, He'll be waiting for me, I won't have to cross Jordan a-lone.
Hum
Hum

10 STANDING SOMEWHERE IN THE SHADOWS

E. J. R. — E. J. Rollings

1. Are there cross-es too heav - y to car - ry, And bur-dens too
2. Are there shad-ows of deep dis - ap - point-ment And trusts that have
3. Has the storm o - ver-shad-owed your sun-shine, And life lost at-
heav-y to bear, Are there heart-aches and tears and an-guish And
prov-en un-true; Has the dark - ness of night set-tled round you, Has your
trac-tion for you, Have the dreams that you cherished been broken, Is your
no one who seems to care?
hope and your faith wavered too?
soul filled with bit-ter-ness too?
CHORUS
Standing somewhere in the shadows you ll find
Je - sus, He's the Friend who always cares and understands. Standing somewhere in the
rit.
shad-ows you will find Him And you'll know Him by the nail-prints in His hands.

11

IN THE GARDEN WITH JESUS

Wm. C. Poole

B. D. Ackley

DUET
1. Have you been in the gar-den with Je - sus, A - lone with the
2. Have you been in the gar-den with Je - sus, And prayed till the
3. Have you been in the gar-den with Je - sus, O say, have you
Sav - ior in prayer? Did the an-gels of heav-en come near you, Was
break of the day, And the glo - ry of heav-en's bright morn-ing Drove
tar - ried in prayer Till the an-gels from heav-en there met you, With
Je - sus a-wait-ing you there?
all of the dark-ness a - way?
Je - sus, the Sav - ior, in prayer?
CHORUS
Have you been in the gar-den with
Je - sus, Have you walked with Him, talked with Him there? . . Have you
been in the gar-den with Je - sus—All a-lone with the Sav-ior in prayer?

BE STILL AND KNOW

Mrs. Hal Buckner

B. B. McKinney

DUET.
1. That He is God, be still and know, Tho' storm-swept be thy wea-ry soul,
2. Tho' shattered hopes surround thee still, Tho' dark and rug - ged be thy way,
3. Thy fears a lov - ing Lord doth know, Thy wounds were His ere they were thine;
4. No depth of storm nor strength of gale Can move thee from thy place se-cure;
Thy deep-est grief to Him is woe, And o - ver all He hath con - trol.
Know thou for thee a Fa-ther's will Doth or - der all things day by day.
In mer - cy doth the Lord be-stow E'en pain if 'twill thy heart en - twine.
His pow'r o'er these doth e'en pre-vail, His boundless love doth e'er en - dure.
CHORUS
Be still and know, be still and know, That He is God, be still and
know; He sees and feels thy deep - est woe, That He is
rit.
God, be still and know.
Coda after last stanza.
That He is God, be still and know.

13 HE'LL UNDERSTAND AND SAY "WELL DONE"

Words and Melody by LUCY E. CAMPBELL — Arr. for JOHN T. BENSON, Jr.

1. If when you give the best of your serv - ice, Tell - ing the
2. Mis - un - der - stood, the Sav - iour of sin - ners, Hung on the
3. If when this life of la - bor is end - ed, And the re-
4. But if you try and fail in your try - ing, Hands sore and

world that the Sav-iour is come; Be not dis-mayed when men don't be-
cross; He was God's on - ly Son; Oh! hear Him call His Fa - ther in
ward; of the race you have run; Oh! take the sweet rest pre-pared for
scarred from the work you've be-gun; Take up your cross, run quick - ly to

lieve you, He un - der - stands; He'll say, "Well done."
heav - en, "Let not my will, but Thine be done."
faith - ful, Will be His blest, and fi - nal, "Well done."
meet Him, He'll un - der - stand, He'll say, "Well done."

CHORUS

Oh, when I come to the end of my jour - ney, Wea - ry of

life and the bat - tle is won; Car - 'ing the staff and the

HE'LL UNDERSTAND AND SAY "WELL DONE"

cross of re-demp-tion, He'll un-der-stand and say "Well done."
14
JUST A CLOSER WALK WITH THEE
As sung by Jimmie Davis
COPYRIGHT, 1943, BY HARRY W. VOM BRUCH
ASSIGNED TO THE RODEHEAVER CO.
Negro Spiritual
Arr. by John Hallett
1. I am weak but Thou art strong, Je - sus keeps me from all wrong,
2. Through this world of toils and snares, If I fal - ter Lord who cares,
3. When my fee - ble life is o'er, Times for me won't be no more,
I'll be sat - is - fied as long, As I walk, Let me walk, close with Thee.
Who with me my bur-den shares, None but Thee, dear Lord, none but Thee.
Guide me gent-ly, safe-ly o'er To Thy king - dom shore, to Thy shore.
Refrain
Just a clos - er walk with Thee; Grant it Je - sus if you please,
rit.
Dai - ly walk - ing close with Thee, Let it be, dear Lord, let it be.

15 I WANT TO BE READY TO MEET HIM

ADGER M. PACE G. T. SPEER

1. You may have your worldly pleas-ures, your sil - ver and your gold, You may
2. Yon may talk a -bout your rich-es, your diamonds and your pearls, You may
3. There is one thing I can boast of, sal - va -tion from the fall, I'm an
pile up all the rich - es that this old world can hold; But I'd rath - er
gain the wealth for a - ges of this and all the worlds, But the Sav - iour
heir to wealth in glo - ry, my Fa-ther owns it all; That is why I'm
D. S.—to meet Him in the sky; Oh, I want to
have my Sav - iour, and with Him firm - ly stand, For I want to be
is more pre - cious, with Him I'll take my stand, For I want to be
shout-ing hap - py and go at His com-mand, For I want to be
be more like Him, and do His blest com - mand, For I want to be
FINE. CHORUS.
read - y to meet Him in the glo - ry land. I want to be
I want to be
read - y to meet Him in the glo - ry - land.
D. S.
read - y to meet Him by and by, I want to be read-y
read - y I want to be read -y

16 MY WONDERFUL LORD

H. L. Haldor Lillenas

1. I have found a deep peace that I nev - er had known And a joy this world
2. I de - sire that my life shall be or-dered by Thee, That my will be in
3. All the tal-ents I have I have laid at Thy feet, Thy ap-prov - al shall
4. Thou art fair - er to me than the fair-est of earth, Thou om-ni - po-tent,
could not af - ford, . . Since I yield-ed con-trol of my bod - y and soul
per - fect ac - cord; . . With Thine own sov'reign will Thy de-sires to ful - fill,
be my re - ward; . . Be my store great or small, I sur-ren-der it all
life - giv-ing Word; . . O Thou An-cient of Days, Thou art wor-thy all praise,
To my won - der-ful, won-der-ful Lord.
My won - der-ful, won - der - ful Lord.
To my won - der-ful, won - der - ful Lord.
My won - der-ful, won - der - ful Lord!
CHORUS
My won - der - ful Lord, my
won - der - ful Lord, By an - gels and ser-aphs in heav - en a - dored; I
bow at Thy shrine, my Sav-ior di - vine, My won-der - ful, won-der-ful Lord.

17 EVERY HEARTBEAT BRINGS ME NEARER HOME

C. A. Gabriel
Herman Voss
and Alfred B. Smith
1. Je - sus said, "Let not your heart be troub - led, Ye be-
2. Je - sus said, "Let not your heart be troub - led, To the
3. Je - sus said, "Let not your heart be troub - led, What-so-
lieve in God, be - lieve in me; In my Fa-ther's house are man - y
Fa - ther's house I am the way; I will pray and He shall send the
e'er ye ask ye shall re - ceive; And my peace shall un - to you be
man - sions, Lo, a place I will pre - pare for thee."
Spir - it, That He may a - bide with you for aye."
giv - en, I have told you that ye might be - lieve."
CHORUS
Ev - 'ry heart - beat brings me near - er than be - fore To the
home and to the Sav - iour I a - dore; 'Tis a com-fort sweet to know,

EVERY HEARTBEAT BRINGS ME NEARER HOME

As I jour-ney here be-low, Ev-'ry heart-beat brings me near-er home.
18
HE'S THE ONE I LOVE
V. B.
Vincent Bennett
1. Christ, the Sav-iour, has suf-fered for me,
2. Christ, the Sav-iour, a-rose from the grave, He's the One I love;
3. Christ as-cend-ed to God's own right hand,
4. Christ, the Sav-iour, is com-ing for me,
For my sin He was nailed to the tree,
Con-q'ring death that my soul He might save, He's the One I love. . . .
And by grace in the Sav-iour I stand, He's the One I love, I love.
And like Him I shall glo-ri-fied be,
Refrain
He's the One I love, . . . He's the One I love; . . . He died to
save me, and now lives to keep me, That's why He's the One that I love (I love).

19 I HAVE BEEN ALONE WITH JESUS

Words used by per.
Mrs. R. R. Forman.
Solo or Unison.
1. I have been a - lone with Je - sus with my head up - on his breast,
2. With a trembling heart I told him while with joy I lin - gered there,
3. Shall I tell you what he told me while I still was wait - ing there?
4. Then he told me I was wel - come ev - er-more with him to stay,
For I was so ver - y wea - ry that I wait - ed there to rest.
All the bur - den of my sor - row and my heav - y weight of care,
For it took a - way my trou - bles and it took a - way my care;
And he said that he would nev - er cast his lov - ing child a - way.
I have been a - lone with Je - sus and he bade me stay a - while, And I
How the voice of Sa - tan's whisp'rings oft - en called me in - to sin, And I
O he told me how he lov'd me tho' a wayward, err - ing child, And I
"Lo!" He said "I am thy Sav - iour, as a rock I firm - ly stand—Come and
felt it ver - y pre - cious in the sunshine of his smile.
asked him if I might not stay for - ev - er there with him.
felt so ver - y hap - py as he look'd on me and smil'd.
rest beneath my shadow in this weary, thirst - y land."
Chorus. Harmony.
I've been alone with Je - sus, My bless - ed, blessed Je - sus, I've been alone with Je - sus, In the sunshine of his smile.

SUBMISSION

C. Austin Miles.
Mrs. R. R. Forman.
Lento.
Solo.
1. The path that I have trod, Has bro't me nearer God, Tho' oft it
2. The cross that I must bear, If I a crown would wear, Is not the
3. Submission to the will Of Him who guides me still Is surety
led........ thro' sorow's gates. Tho' not the way I'd choose, In my way I might lose
cross..... that I should take; But, since on me 'tis laid, I'll take it, un - a - fraid,
of......... His love revealed; My soul shall rise a-bove This world in which I move;
The joy that yet for me a - waits.
And bear it for the Mas-ter's sake.
I con-quer on - ly where I yield.
Refrain.
Not what I wish to be, Nor where I
accel.
a tempo.
wish to go, For who am I that I should choose my way? The Lord shall
choose for me, 'Tis bet-ter far, I know, So let Him bid me go, or stay.

21 NOTHING SATISFIES BUT JESUS

Mrs. C. H. Morris | Mrs. C. H. Morris

1. Noth-ing sat-is-fies but Je-sus, Bread of life to mor-tals giv'n;
2. Since I heard the voice of Je-sus, Since mine eyes be-held the King,
3. With His joy my heart is thrill-ing, All my hope in Him I see;
May His pres-ence now re-fresh us Like the morn-ing dew from Heav'n!
All my love, my heart's af-fec-tion, All I have, to Him I bring.
Doubt, and gloom, and fear dis-pel-ling, Christ is All in all to me.
CHORUS.
Give me Je-sus, give me Je-sus, Take the world, but give me Je-sus,
Give me Je-sus, give me Je-sus,
To sat-is-fy . . with ev-'ry blessing, His love and peace my soul pos-sess-ing;
To all be-side, my heart re-plies: There's naught but Jesus sat-is-fies! A-MEN.

SATISFIED

Mattie B. Shannon
Adam Geibel
Solo *ad lib.*
1. When the cross that God my Fa - ther gives So ver - y heav - y seems, And when I see the blighting, Find the ashes of my dreams; When the heart that beats with- in my breast Is wea - ry and cast down, And when the sun is shadowed, While the heav - ens seem to frown;
2. When the treas-ures I have striv - en for Are slip-ping fast a - way; When e - vil tempts me sorely And so anx-ious is my day; When the fier-y darts that Satan sends Are crowding thick and fast, And when youth's hopes are shattered And lie dy - ing in the blast;
3. When the cares and tri - als of this life Are press-ing more and more; When death's dark an-gel softly Spreads his wings above my door; When the paths that e'er my feet must tread So dark and drear - y grow, And when my soul is heav - y With a name-less pain and woe;
Refrain
O I think of Christ my Sav-iour; And the cross on Calv-'ry's side, I think of what He bore for me, And am straightway satisfied.

23

THEY LED HIM AWAY

Herbert Buffum and C. H. G

Chas. H. Gabriel.

M. 116 = ♩
1 They led Him a-way to be cru - ci - fied, The meek and low - ly
2. They led Him a-way—nor did He re - bel, The great, re-deem-ing
3. They led Him a-way—and He died for me, The lov - ing, liv - ing
Je - sus! And there on the cross, between thieves He died, My won - der - ful,
Je - sus! The an-guish He suf-fered no tongue can tell This won - der - ful,
Je - sus! I'll fol - low His steps till His face I see, This won - der - ful,
CHORUS.
won - der - ful Je - sus. They led Him a - way, they led Him a - way
To Cal - va - ry's rug - ged cross! . . . . . . He fol - lowed, a - lone,
dim.
ad lib.
Our sins to a - tone, This won - der - ful, won - der - ful Je - sus.

O MY SOUL, BLESS THOU JEHOVAH

ARR. COPYRIGHT 1907, RENEWAL 1935
THE RODEHEAVER CO., OWNER
Psalm 103.
From Donizetti,
by J. B. Herbert.
DUET. M. 66 = ♩
1. O my soul, bless thou Je - ho - vah, All with - in me bless His name;
2. He will not for-ev - er chide us, Nor keep an - ger in His mind;
3. Far as east is from west dis-tant, He hath put a - way our sins;
Bless Je-ho - vah, and for-get not All His mer - cies to pro - claim.
Hath not dealt as we of - fend - ed, Nor re-ward - ed as we sinned.
Like the pit - y of a fa - ther, Hath the Lord's com-pas-sion been.
CHORUS.
For as high.......... as is the heav - en, Far a-
For as high as is the heav - en,
bove......... the earth be - low, Ev - er great to them that
Far a - bove the earth be - low,
fear Him Is the mer - cy He will ev - er, ev - er show.

BACK OF THE CLOUDS

C. R. F. — Carolyn R. Freeman

DUET. Soprano and Alto
1. Nev-er fear tho' shad-ows dark a-round your path may fall; Do not let your heart be trou - - bled; From His throne in heav-en, God is watch-ing one and all, . . He will ev-er care for you. . . . . .
2. Win-ter long is o-ver and the spring has gone her way, Oft-en have the storm-clouds gath - - ered, But the rain has on-ly made the blos-soms look more gay, . . Giv-en earth a bright-er hue. . . . .
3. Keep the light of hope e-ter-nal dwell-ing in your heart, Rest up-on the Fa-ther's prom - - ise, And you'll find that care and trou-ble quick-ly will de-part, . . Heaven's peace will en-ter in. . . . . .
care for you,
CHORUS All, in two parts
Back of the clouds the sun is al-ways shin-ing, Aft-er the storms your skies will all be blue;
(Simile)
Four Parts
God has pre-pared a
pre-pared

BACK OF THE CLOUDS
ros - y - tint - ed lin - ing, Back of the clouds it's wait - ing to shine thru.
26
CLEANSE ME
Edwin Orr
Maori Melody by John McNeill
1. Search me, O God,........ and know my heart to - day;......
2. I praise Thee, Lord,........ for cleans - ing me from sin:......
3. Lord, take my life,......... and make it whol - ly Thine:....
4. O Ho - ly Ghost,....... re - viv - al comes from Thee:.....
Try me, O Sav - ior, know my thoughts, I pray:....
Ful - fill Thy Word, and make me pure with - in;......
Fill my poor heart with Thy great love di - vine;....
Send a re - viv - al— start the work in me:.....
See if there be........ some wick - ed way in me:.....
Fill me with fire,...... where once I burned with shame:...
Take all my will,...... my pas - sion, self and pride;....
Thy Word de - clares...... Thou wilt sup - ply our need:....
Cleanse me from ev - 'ry sin, and set me free.......
Grant my de - sire to mag - ni - fy Thy name......
I now sur - ren - der: Lord, in me a - bide.......
For bless - ing now, O Lord, I hum - bly plead.......

27

HE TENDERLY LOOKED AT ME

F. F. D.

F. F. Dawdy

Solo
1. When Je - sus a - lone was stand-ing, By all His friends for - got,
2. When drift-ing a - way in dark - ness, Lost in the black - est night,
3. They took my bless-ed Sav - ior Out to the moun-tain side,
And Pe - ter, near by, de - ny - ing, Say - ing, "I know Him not,"
Out on the sea of sor - row, Far from the Bless - ed Light,
And nailed Him there to the cross-tree, Je - sus, the Cru - ci - fied.
'Twas then he saw the Sav - ior Look at him ten - der - ly;
I heard a sweet voice call - ing, Call - ing from o'er the sea,
And when I saw my Sav - ior, Dy - ing on Cal - va - ry,
And then, re-mem-b'ring the say - ing, Went and wept bit - ter - ly.
And then I saw my Sav - ior Ten - der - ly look at me.
He drew me gra-cious - ly to Him, By His kind look at me.
Chorus
He ten - der-ly looked at me, He ten - der-ly looked at me,
at me, at me,

HE TENDERLY LOOKED AT ME
He drew me gra-cious-ly to Him, When He ten-der-ly looked at me.
28
WE SHALL SHINE AS THE STARS
J. W. V.
J. W. Van DeVenter
1. We may tar-ry a while here as strangers, Un-no-ticed by those who pass by;
2. We may nev-er be rich in earth's treasures, Nor rise on the lad-der of fame;
3. We may live in a tent or a cot-tage, And die in se-clu-sion a-lone;
But the Sav-ior will crown us in glo-ry, To shine as the stars of the sky.
But the saints will at last be re-ward-ed, Made rich in Im-man-u-el's name.
But the Fa-ther who see-eth in se-cret, Re-mem-bers each one of His own.
CHORUS
We shall shine as the stars of the morn-ing, With Je-sus the Cru-ci-fied One;
We shall rise to be like Him for-ev-er, E-ter-nal-ly shine as the sun.

29 THE HEART THAT WAS BROKEN FOR ME

J. W. V. — J. W. VanDeVenter.

Duet.

1. There came from the skies in the days long a - go The Lord with a mes-sage of love; . . . . The world knew Him not, He was treated with scorn—This won-der-ful gift from a - bove. . . .
2. He came to His own— to the ones that He lov'd; The sheep that had wander'd a - stray; . . . . They heard not His voice, but the friend of mankind Was hat-ed and driv-en a - way. . . .
3. The birds have their nests, and the fox - es have holes, But He had no place for His head; . . . . A pal - let of stone on the cold mountain side Was all that He had for His bed. . . .
4. I can - not re - ject such a Sav - iour as He; Dis - hon - or and wound Him a - gain; . . . . I'll go to His feet and re - pent of my sin, Be will-ing to suf-fer the pain. . . .

Chorus.

They crown'd Him with thorns, He was beaten with stripes; He was smit-ten and nail'd to the tree, (to the tree.) But the pain in His heart was the hard-est to bear, The heart that was broken for me.

4. I'll take up my cross, I will walk by His side, For the path-way of du - ty I see, (yes, I see,) I will fol - low my Lord and a - bide in His heart, The heart that was broken for me. . . . .

rit.

for me.

THINE, LORD

Robert Harkness
Robert Harkness
Solo
1. When I think of Je - sus dy - ing on the cross for me,
2. When I think of Je - sus ris - ing vic - tor o'er the tomb,
3. When I think of Je - sus, com - ing back to earth a - gain,
Thine, Lord, would I be; Free - ly giv - ing up His life from
Thine, Lord, would I be; As the Lord tri - umph - ant - ly dis-
Thine, Lord, would I be. Com - ing in great glo - ry as the
sin to set me free, Thine, Lord, would I be.
pers - ing death's dark gloom Thine, Lord, would I be.
King of kings to reign, Thine, Lord, would I be.
Refrain
Thine, Lord, on - ly Thine, Thine, Lord, on - ly Thine. Take me, use me as Thou
wilt dear Sav - iour, Thine, Lord, on - ly Thine, Thine, Lord, on - ly Thine.
pp

31 ON A RUGGED HILL

K.W. KEITH WHITFORD

Solo
1. On a rug - ged hill stood a rug - ged cross,
2. On a rug - ged hill stood a mock - ing throng,
And up - on that cross there hung in shame God's be - lov - ed Son,
Scorn - ing Him who came to save the lost. It was not in vain
Christ the love - ly one Who from heav - en to the sin - ner came.
that the Sav - iour came To re - deem the world at price - less cost.
CHORUS
Cal - v'ry - rug - ged hill of sor - row Where the Prince of
glo - ry died for me; Wound - ed - crushed and brok - en -
heart - ed 'Lone He suf - fered un - told ag - o - ny

ON A RUGGED HILL

Sin - less - there He bore my bur - dens That from sin - ful
shame I might be free
Glor - ious day - He
took my sins a - way On the cross of Cal - va - ry.
32
WONDROUS PEACE
R.H.
ROBERT HARKNESS
Rest - ing in love di - vine, peace, wondrous peace is mine, Naught can my
soul dis - tress, Though cares and sor - row press; Peace, per - fect peace is mine,
gift of my Lord di - vine, Thro' all e - ter - ni - ty, peace, per - fect peace.

33

ALL THE WAY

Rev. W. C. Poole — Chas. H. Gabriel

1. How far shall I go for the sheep a-stray, I asked of my Shep - herd true; His an - swer came back, it was "All the way I went in my love for you." (for you.")
2. How long shall I seek, for the night comes on, I see not a sin - gle track; My Shep - herd re - plied, "Thro' the night a - lone I sought till I brought you back." (you back.")
3. How far shall I go, for the way is wild, And rough is the rock - y steep; My Shep - herd re - plied, "Go as far, my child, As wan - ders my stray - ing sheep." (my sheep.")
4. No lon - ger I feared the long rough way, I want -ed His way to know, And loud - ly I cried, "Help me, Lord, I pray, As far as you went, to go." (to go.")

CHORUS

All the way, all the way, And noth - ing less will do;...... To save the lost, count not the cost, 'Twas the way of your Lord for you.

I'LL SING IT TODAY

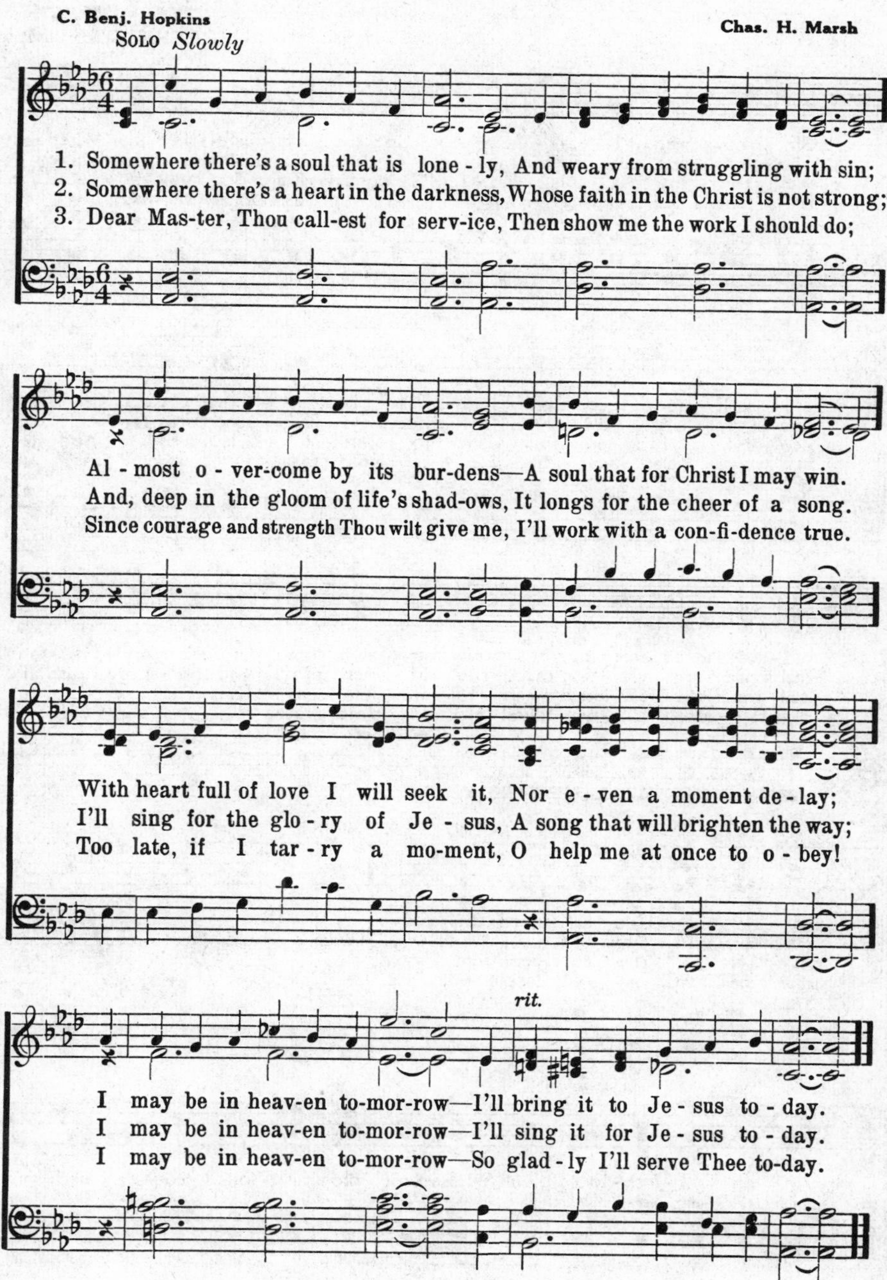
C. Benj. Hopkins
Chas. H. Marsh
SOLO Slowly
1. Somewhere there's a soul that is lone-ly, And weary from struggling with sin;
2. Somewhere there's a heart in the darkness, Whose faith in the Christ is not strong;
3. Dear Mas-ter, Thou call-est for serv-ice, Then show me the work I should do;
Al-most o-ver-come by its bur-dens—A soul that for Christ I may win.
And, deep in the gloom of life's shad-ows, It longs for the cheer of a song.
Since courage and strength Thou wilt give me, I'll work with a con-fi-dence true.
With heart full of love I will seek it, Nor e-ven a moment de-lay;
I'll sing for the glo-ry of Je-sus, A song that will brighten the way;
Too late, if I tar-ry a mo-ment, O help me at once to o-bey!
rit.
I may be in heav-en to-mor-row—I'll bring it to Je-sus to-day.
I may be in heav-en to-mor-row—I'll sing it for Je-sus to-day.
I may be in heav-en to-mor-row—So glad-ly I'll serve Thee to-day.

35 THE OLD-FASHIONED MEETING

H. B. HERBERT BUFFUM

1. Oh, how well I re-mem-ber in the old-fash-ioned days, When some old-fash-ioned peo-ple had some old-fash-ioned ways; In the old-fash-ioned meet-ings, as they tar-ried there, In the old-fash-ioned man-ner, how God an-swered their pray'r.
2. There was sing-ing, such sing-ing, of those old-fash-ioned airs! There was pow-er, such pow-er in those old-fash-ioned pray'rs, An old-fashioned con-vic-tion made the sin-ner pray, And the Lord heard and saved Him, in the old-fash-ioned way.
3. Well, they say it is bet-ter, "Things have changed don't you know," And the peo-ple in gen-ral, seem to think it is so; And they call me old-fash-ioned when I dare to say, That I like it far bet-ter in the old-fash-ioned way.
4. If the Lord nev-er chang-es, as the fash-ions of men, If He's al-ways the same, why, He is old-fash-ioned, then! As an old-fash-ioned sin-ner saved thro old-time grace, Oh, I'm sure He will take me to an old-fash-ioned place.
CHORUS
'Twas an old-fash-ioned meet-ing, in an old-fash-ioned place, Where some old-fash-ioned peo-ple had some

THE OLD-FASHIONED MEETING

old - fash - ioned grace: As an old - fash - ioned sin - ner I be - gan to
pray, And God heard me, and saved me in the old - fash - ioned way.
36 WE SHALL SEE HIS LOVELY FACE
N. J. C.
NORMAN J. CLAYTON
1. We shall see His love - ly face Some bright, gold-en morn - ing, When the clouds have rift - ed And the shades have flown; Sor - row will be turned to joy, Heart-aches gone for- ev - er; No more night, on - ly light, When we see His face.
2. God shall wipe a - way all tears Some bright, gold en morn - ing, When the jour-ney's end- ed, And the course is run; No more cry - ing, pain or death In that home of glad-ness, Tri - als cease, all is peace, When we see His face.
3. We shall meet to part no more, Some bright, gold-en morn - ing, At the gates of glo - ry Where our loved ones stand; Songs of vic - t'ry fill the skies In that hour of greet-ing, End-less days, end - less praise, When we see His face.

37 I HAVE BEEN SAVED

Ina Duley Ogdon
Chas. H. Gabriel
1. My glad heart is sing-ing by day and by night, My soul o-ver-
2. O would that my tongue with His truth were a-flame, For life would I
3. His mer-cy, His good-ness can nev-er be told, And heav-en a-
flows with a won-drous de-light, My joy would I share with a sin-wea-ry race,
give by the pow'r of His name; Some day I shall look on His beau-ti-ful face,
lone shall His glo-ries un-fold, And there He has gone to prepare me a place,
For I have been saved by grace.
CHORUS
Saved! hal-le-lu-jah!
I have been
Saved! hal-le-lu-jah!
I have been
Saved by His won-der-ful, mar-vel-ous grace!
I'll sing of His love till I meet Him a-bove, For I have been saved by grace.

38

THE SANDS OF TIME

RUTHERFORD

ANNE ROSS COUSIN

CHRETIENE D'URHAN
Arr. by E. F. RIMBAULT

1. The sands of time are sink - ing, The dawn of heav - en breaks;
2. O Christ! He is the foun - tain, The deep, sweet well of love!
3. Oh, I am my Be - lov - ed's, And my Be - lov - ed's mine!
4. The Bride eyes not her gar - ment, But her dear Bridegroom's face;
The sum - mer morn I've sighed for, The fair, sweet morn a - wakes:
The streams on earth I've tast - ed, More deep I'll drink a - bove:
He brings a poor vile sin - ner In - to His "house of wine."
I will not gaze at glo - ry, But on my King of grace.
Dark, dark hath been the mid - night, But day - spring is at hand,
There, to an o - cean ful - ness, His mer - cy doth ex - pand,
I stand up - on His mer - it, I know no oth - er stand,
Not at the crown He giv - eth, But on His pierc - ed hand,
And glo - ry, glo - ry dwell - eth In Im - man - uel's land.
And glo - ry, glo - ry dwell - eth In Im - man - uel's land.
Not e'en where glo - ry dwell - eth In Im - mau - uel's land.
The Lamb is all the glo - ry Of Im - man - uel's land. A-MEN.

39 HE'S NEAR, YES, EVER NEAR

Gerald E. Bonney — Gerald E. Bonney

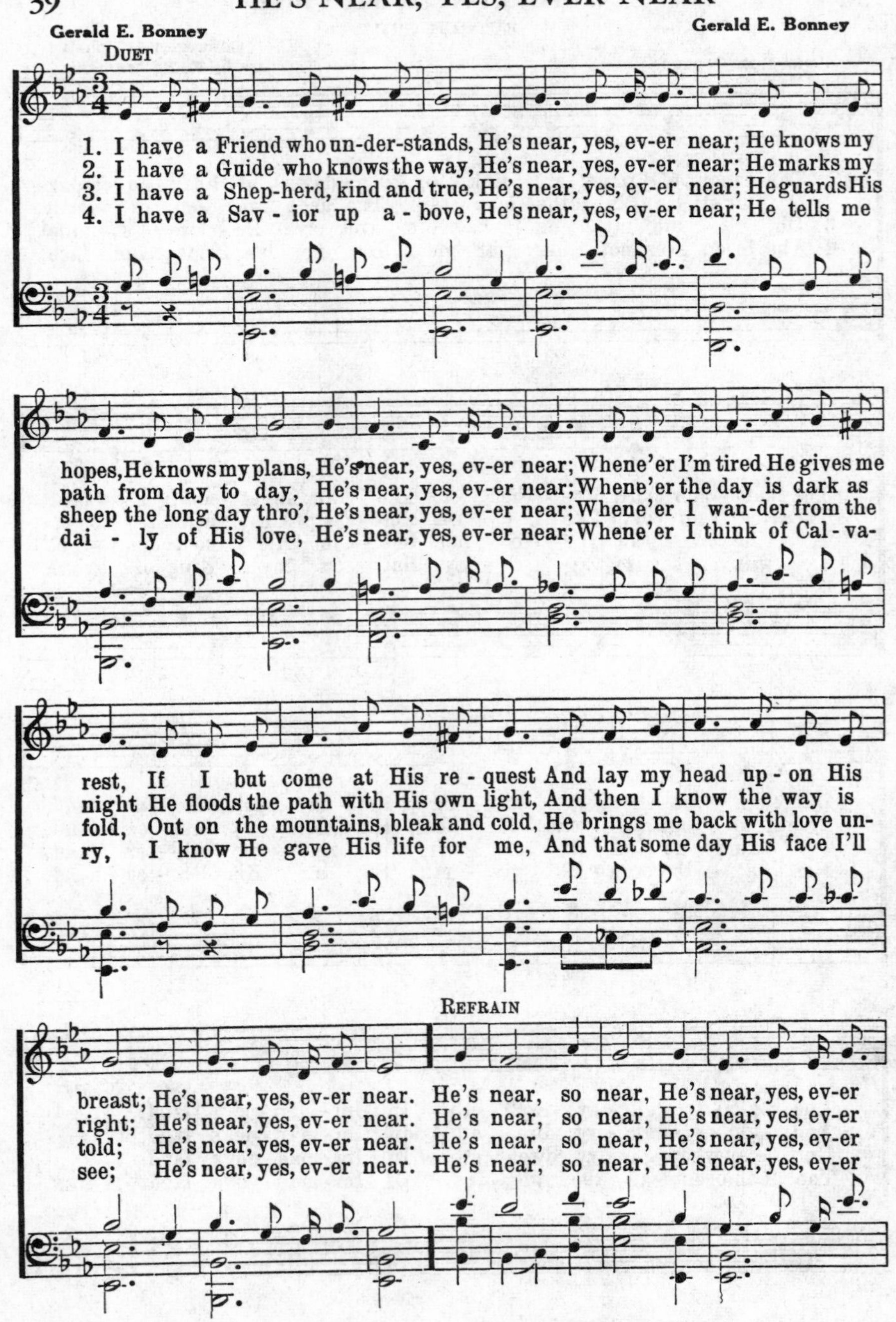
DUET
1. I have a Friend who un-der-stands, He's near, yes, ev-er near; He knows my
2. I have a Guide who knows the way, He's near, yes, ev-er near; He marks my
3. I have a Shep-herd, kind and true, He's near, yes, ev-er near; He guards His
4. I have a Sav - ior up a - bove, He's near, yes, ev-er near; He tells me
hopes, He knows my plans, He's near, yes, ev-er near; Whene'er I'm tired He gives me
path from day to day, He's near, yes, ev-er near; Whene'er the day is dark as
sheep the long day thro', He's near, yes, ev-er near; Whene'er I wan-der from the
dai - ly of His love, He's near, yes, ev-er near; Whene'er I think of Cal - va-
rest, If I but come at His re - quest And lay my head up - on His
night He floods the path with His own light, And then I know the way is
fold, Out on the mountains, bleak and cold, He brings me back with love un-
ry, I know He gave His life for me, And that some day His face I'll
REFRAIN
breast; He's near, yes, ev-er near. He's near, so near, He's near, yes, ev-er
right; He's near, yes, ev-er near. He's near, so near, He's near, yes, ev-er
told; He's near, yes, ev-er near. He's near, so near, He's near, yes, ev-er
see; He's near, yes, ev-er near. He's near, so near, He's near, yes, ev-er

HE'S NEAR, YES, EVER NEAR

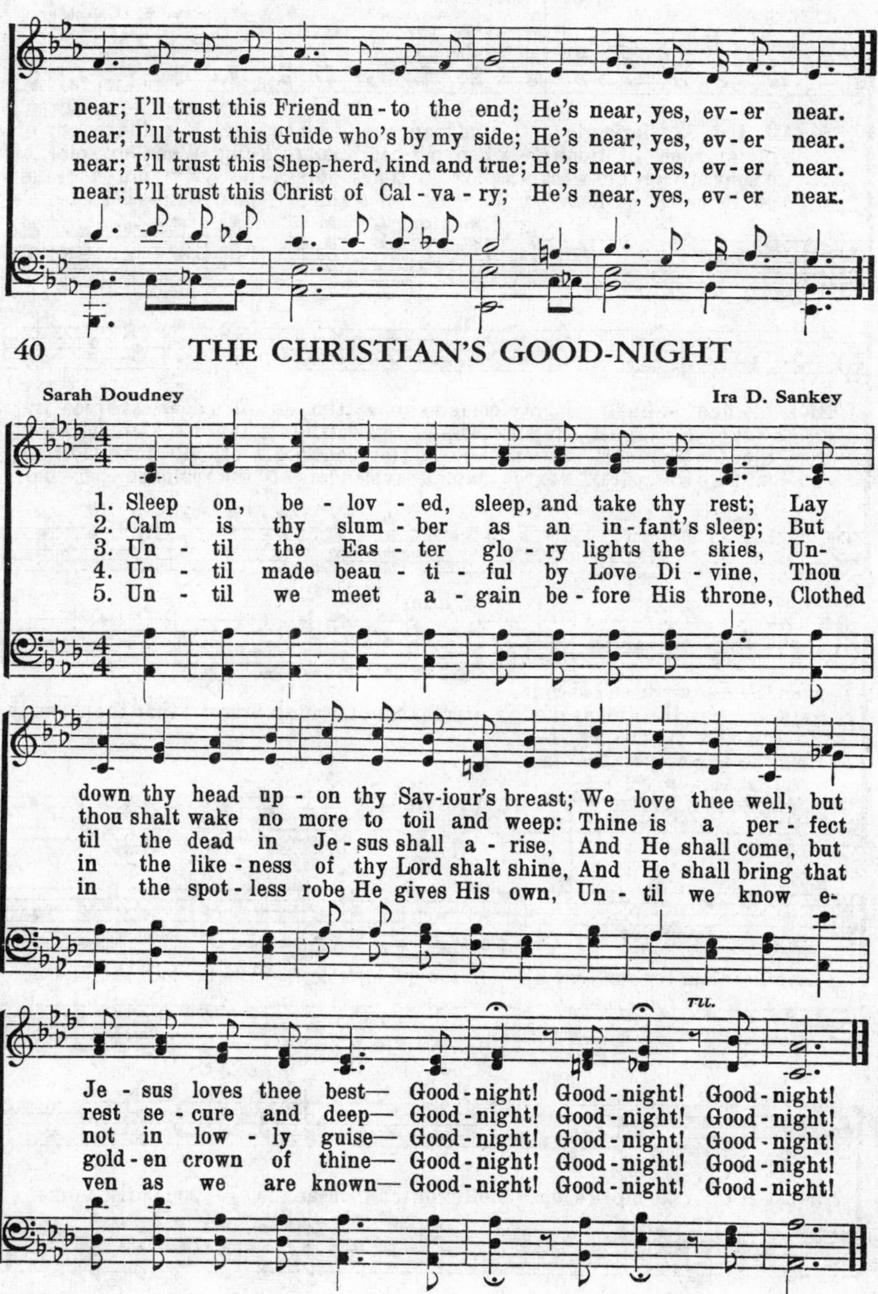
near; I'll trust this Friend un - to the end; He's near, yes, ev - er near.
near; I'll trust this Guide who's by my side; He's near, yes, ev - er near.
near; I'll trust this Shep-herd, kind and true; He's near, yes, ev - er near.
near; I'll trust this Christ of Cal - va - ry; He's near, yes, ev - er near.
40 THE CHRISTIAN'S GOOD-NIGHT
Sarah Doudney
Ira D. Sankey
1. Sleep on, be - lov - ed, sleep, and take thy rest; Lay
2. Calm is thy slum - ber as an in - fant's sleep; But
3. Un - til the Eas - ter glo - ry lights the skies, Un-
4. Un - til made beau - ti - ful by Love Di - vine, Thou
5. Un - til we meet a - gain be - fore His throne, Clothed
down thy head up - on thy Sav-iour's breast; We love thee well, but
thou shalt wake no more to toil and weep: Thine is a per - fect
til the dead in Je - sus shall a - rise, And He shall come, but
in the like - ness of thy Lord shalt shine, And He shall bring that
in the spot - less robe He gives His own, Un - til we know e-
rit.
Je - sus loves thee best— Good - night! Good - night! Good - night!
rest se - cure and deep— Good - night! Good - night! Good - night!
not in low - ly guise— Good - night! Good - night! Good - night!
gold - en crown of thine— Good - night! Good - night! Good - night!
ven as we are known— Good - night! Good - night! Good - night!

41 CHIEFEST OF TEN THOUSAND

A. H. A. Rev. A. H. Ackley

1. All the Sav-ior's glo - ry mind can nev - er meas-ure, Nor the tongue of
2. Mine in time of troub - le when my heart is break-ing, When my spir - it
3. He's my strength in weakness, joy in times of sad - ness, My pro - tec - tion
4. And in earth or heav - en there is not His e - qual, Saints nor an - gels
man de-fine (de-fine); I have come to know Him as life's dear-est treas-ure,
droops with grief (with grief), He with bless-ed com-fort heals the bit - ter ach - ing,
from the foe (the foe), Patient, kind and lov-ing, heart of all my glad-ness,
can com-pare (compare), Nor the matchless splendors of the realm su - per - nal,
Know Him as my friend di-vine.
Swift and sure He brings relief.
He dis-pels my ev - 'ry foe.
He's the fair-est of the fair.
CHORUS
Fairer than the morning, brighter than the noonday,
Love-lier than the sun - set up - on the qui - et sea, Pur - er than the lil - y,
sweet-er than the bird's song, Chiefest of ten thousand is Je - sus Christ to me.

SATISFIED WITH JESUS

B. B. McK.
B. B. McKinney
Slowly
1. I am sat - is - fied with Je - sus, He has done so much for me,
2. He is with me in my tri - als, Best of friends of all is He;
3. I can hear the voice of Je - sus Call-ing out so plead-ing-ly,
4. When my work on earth is end - ed, And I cross the mys - tic sea,
He has suf - fered to re - deem me, He has died to set me free.
I can al-ways count on Je - sus, Can He al-ways count on me?
"Go and win the lost and stray - ing;" Is He sat - is - fied with me?
Oh, that I could hear Him say - ing, "I am sat - is - fied with thee."
Chorus
I am sat - is - fied, I am sat - is - fied, I am sat - is-
fied with Je - sus, But the ques - tion comes to me, As I
think of Cal - va - ry, Is my Mas - ter sat - is - fied with me?
rit.

TAKE UP THY CROSS

A. H. A. REV. A. H. ACKLEY.

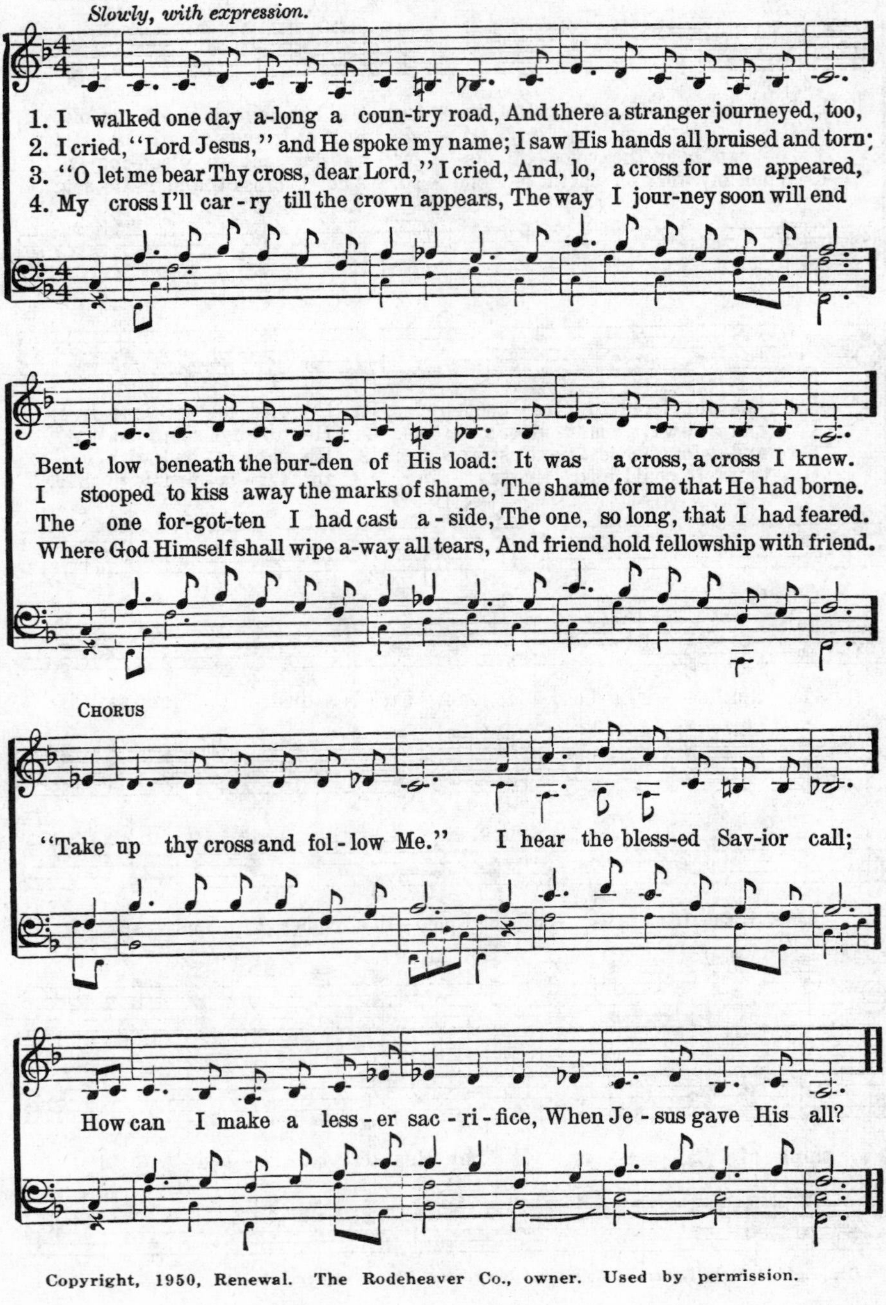

Slowly, with expression.

1. I walked one day a-long a coun-try road, And there a stranger journeyed, too,
2. I cried, "Lord Jesus," and He spoke my name; I saw His hands all bruised and torn;
3. "O let me bear Thy cross, dear Lord," I cried, And, lo, a cross for me appeared,
4. My cross I'll car-ry till the crown appears, The way I jour-ney soon will end

Bent low beneath the bur-den of His load: It was a cross, a cross I knew.
I stooped to kiss away the marks of shame, The shame for me that He had borne.
The one for-got-ten I had cast a-side, The one, so long, that I had feared.
Where God Himself shall wipe a-way all tears, And friend hold fellowship with friend.

CHORUS

"Take up thy cross and fol-low Me." I hear the bless-ed Sav-ior call;
How can I make a less-er sac-ri-fice, When Je-sus gave His all?

READY

S. E. L. — CHARLIE D. TILLMAN

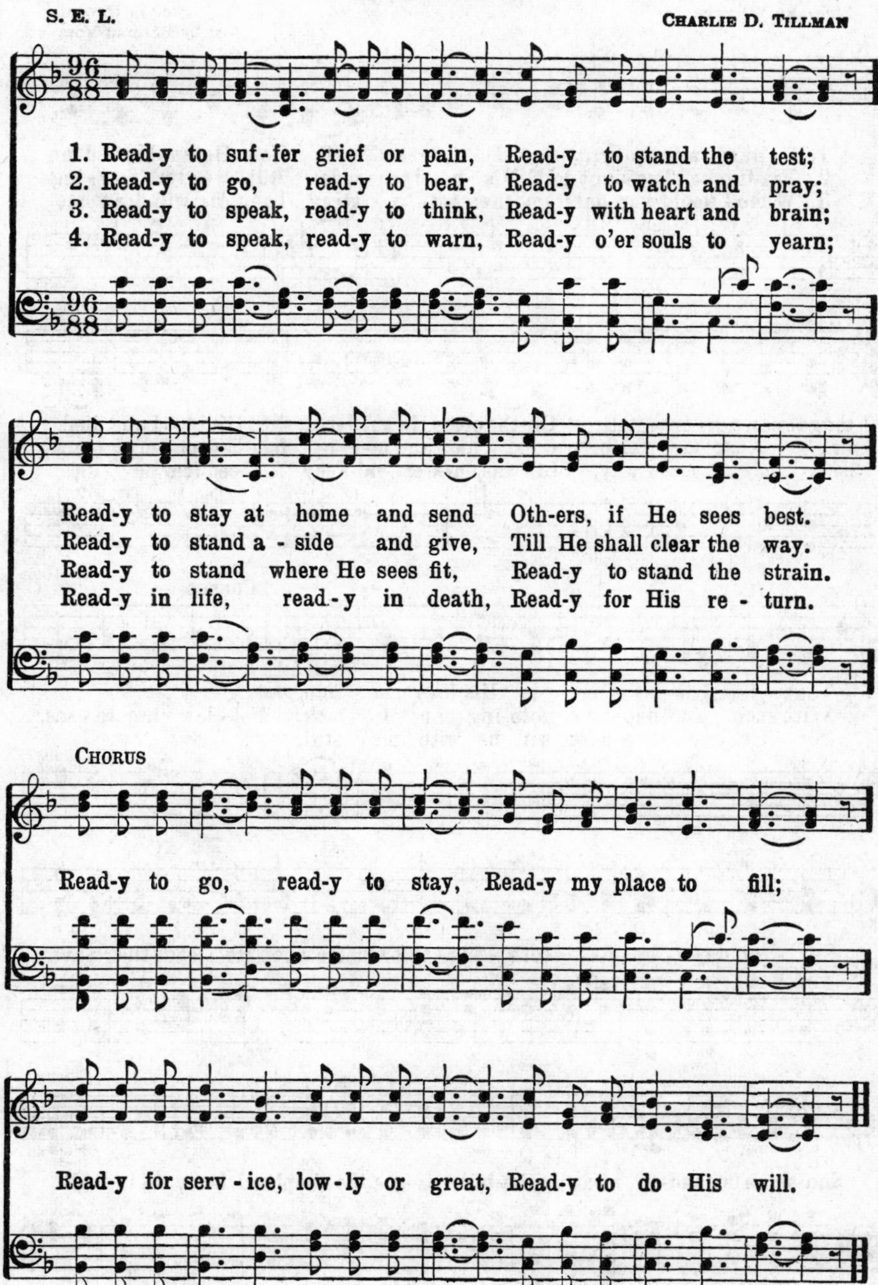
1. Read-y to suf-fer grief or pain, Read-y to stand the test;
2. Read-y to go, read-y to bear, Read-y to watch and pray;
3. Read-y to speak, read-y to think, Read-y with heart and brain;
4. Read-y to speak, read-y to warn, Read-y o'er souls to yearn;
Read-y to stay at home and send Oth-ers, if He sees best.
Read-y to stand a - side and give, Till He shall clear the way.
Read-y to stand where He sees fit, Read-y to stand the strain.
Read-y in life, read-y in death, Read-y for His re - turn.
CHORUS
Read-y to go, read-y to stay, Read-y my place to fill;
Read-y for serv - ice, low-ly or great, Read-y to do His will.

FOLLOWING JESUS

LEONARD WEAVER — M. E. UPHAM
Arr. by Herman Voss

1. I have a Shep-herd, One I love so well, How He has blessed me
2. Pas-tures a-bun-dant doth His hand pro-vide, Still wa-ters flow-ing
3. When I would wan-der from the path a-stray, Then He will draw me

tongue can nev-er tell; On the cross He suf-fered, shed His blood and died,
ev-er at my side, Good-ness and mer-cy fol-low on my track,
back in-to the way; In the dark-est val-ley I need fear no ill,

That I might ev-er in His love con-fide.
With such a Shep-herd noth-ing can I lack.
For He, my Shep-herd, will be with me still.

CHORUS

Fol-low-ing Je-sus,
ev-er day by day,—Noth-ing can harm me when He leads the way;
Sun-shine or shad-ow, what-e'er be-fall—Je-sus, the Shepherd, is my All in All.

MY MOTHER'S BIBLE

Evangelist M. B. WILLIAMS — CHARLIE D. TILLMAN

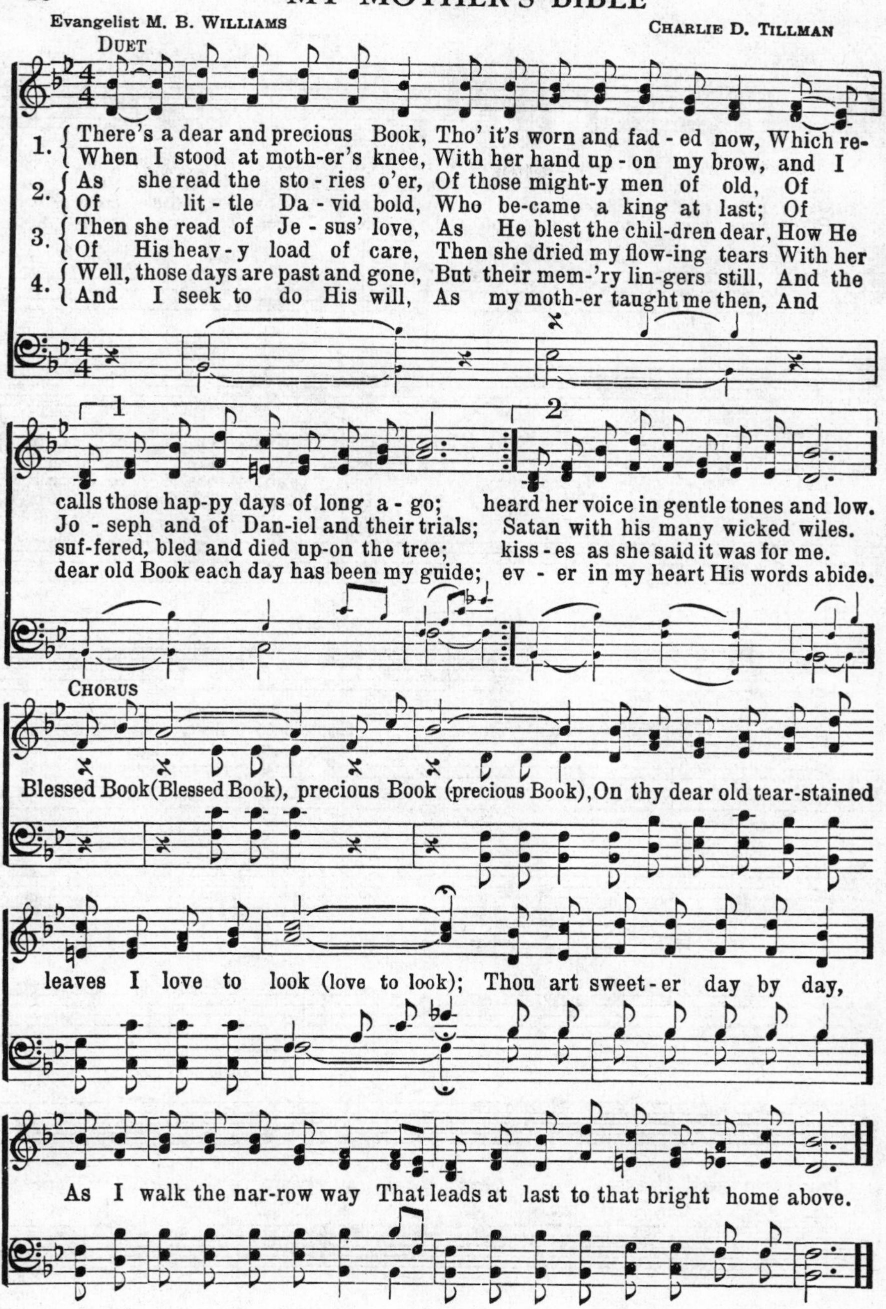
DUET
1. { There's a dear and precious Book, Tho' it's worn and fad - ed now, Which re-
When I stood at moth-er's knee, With her hand up - on my brow, and I
2. { As she read the sto - ries o'er, Of those might-y men of old, Of
Of lit - tle Da - vid bold, Who be-came a king at last; Of
3. { Then she read of Je - sus' love, As He blest the chil-dren dear, How He
Of His heav - y load of care, Then she dried my flow-ing tears With her
4. { Well, those days are past and gone, But their mem-'ry lin-gers still, And the
And I seek to do His will, As my moth-er taught me then, And
1
2
calls those hap-py days of long a - go; heard her voice in gentle tones and low.
Jo - seph and of Dan-iel and their trials; Satan with his many wicked wiles.
suf-fered, bled and died up-on the tree; kiss - es as she said it was for me.
dear old Book each day has been my guide; ev - er in my heart His words abide.
CHORUS
Blessed Book (Blessed Book), precious Book (precious Book), On thy dear old tear-stained
leaves I love to look (love to look); Thou art sweet - er day by day,
As I walk the nar-row way That leads at last to that bright home above.

47 A HEART LIKE THINE

J. W. V.
J. W. VANDEVENTER
1. Give me a love that knows no ill, Give me the grace to
2. On - ly a joy, a few brief years, On - ly a dream, a
3. O - pen mine eyes that I may see, Show me the cross of
4. Pil - low my head up - on Thy breast, Shel - ter my soul and
do.... Thy will; Par - don and cleanse this soul of mine,
vale.. of tears; Vain is this world I now re - sign,
Cal - va - ry; There may I go and not re - pine,
give.. me rest; Fill me with love as I re - cline,
CHORUS
Give me a heart like Thine.... Come to my soul, bless - ed
Je - sus, Hear me! O Sav - ior di - vine!..... O - pen the
like Thine.......
foun - tain and cleanse me, Give me a heart, a heart like Thine.
like Thine.......

FOR ALL MY SIN

N. J. C. NORMAN J. CLAYTON

1. It was His love for me, That nailed Him to the tree, To die in ag - o - ny, For all my sin; For my own guilt and blame, The great Re - deem - er came; Will - ing to bear the shame Of all my sin.
2. To Cal-v'ry's hill one day, The Lord was led a - way, None else the price could pay, For all my sin; He on the cross was slain, Yield - ing His life in pain; He felt the bit - ter stain, Of all my sin.
3. Was ev - er love so strong? Was ev - er crime so wrong? When Je - sus suf - fered long, For all my sin; He saw my great - est need, Be - came my friend in - deed, Thru Him I have been freed, Of all my sin.
CHORUS
O, what a Sav - iour is mine! In Him God's mer - cies com - bine, His love can nev - er de - cline, And He loves me.

49 ASHAMED OF JESUS

JOSEPH GRIGGS
E. O. EXCELL
Arr. by HERMAN VOSS
1. Je - sus, and shall it ev - er be A mor - tal man a-
2. A - shamed of Je - sus! soon - er far Let eve - ning blush to
3. A - shamed of Je - sus! that dear Friend, On whom my hopes of
4. A - shamed of Je - sus! yes, I may, When I've no guilt to
shamed of Thee? A - shamed of Thee, whom an - gels praise, Whose
own a star; He sheds the beams of light di - vine O'er
heav'n de - pend! No! when I blush, be this my shame, That
wash a - way; No tear to wipe, no good to crave, No
glo - ries shine thro' end - less days.
this be - night - ed soul of mine.
I no more re - vere His name.
fears to quell, no soul to save.
CHORUS
A - shamed . . . . of
A - shamed of Je - sus, a-
Je - sus, I nev - er, I nev - er will be; . . . . For
shamed of Je - sus, I nev - er will be; For
Je - - sus, my Sav - iour, is not a - shamed of me.
Je - sus, my Sav - iour, for Je - sus, my Sav - iour,

50 THE SAVIOR CAN SOLVE EVERY PROBLEM

Rev. Oswald J. Smith — B. D. Ackley

1. The Sav-ior can lift ev-'ry bur-den, The heav-y as well as the light;
2. The Sav-ior can bear ev-'ry sor-row, In Him there is com-fort and rest;
3. The Sav-ior can strengthen the wea-ry, His grace is suf-fi-cient for all;
4. The Sav-ior can break sin's do-min-ion, The vic-t'ry He won long a-go;
5. The Sav-ior can sat-is-fy ful-ly The heart that the world can-not fill;
His strength is made per-fect in weak-ness, In Him there is pow-er and might.
No mat-ter how great the af-flic-tion, He on-ly per-mits what is best.
He knows ev-'ry step of the path-way, And lis-tens to hear when we call.
In Him there is free-dom from bondage, He's a-ble to con-quer the foe.
His pres-ence will sanc-ti-fy whol-ly The soul that is yield-ed and still.
CHORUS
ritard.
The Sav-ior can solve ev-'ry problem, The tan-gles of life can un-do;
He can un-do;
rall.
There is noth-ing too hard for Je-sus, There is noth-ing that He can-not do.

JESUS TOOK MY BURDEN

Rev. Johnson Oatman Jr. — Bertha Mae Lillenas

1. When I, a poor, lost sin-ner, Be-fore the Lord did fall, And in the name of
2. Oft-times the way is drear-y, And rugged seems the road, Oft-times I'm weak and
3. When I was crushed with sorrow I bowed in deep de-spair, My load of grief and
4. I'll trust Him for the fu-ture, He know-eth all the way, For with His eye He'll
Je - sus For par-don loud did call; He heard my sup-pli-ca-tion, And
wea - ry, When bent beneath some load; But when I cry in weak-ness, "How
heart-ache Seemed more than I could bear; 'Twas then I heard a whis-per, "You
guide me A - long life's pil-grim way; And I will tell in heav-en, While
soon the weak was strong, For Je-sus took my bur-den, And left me with a song.
long, O Lord, how long?" Then Je-sus takes the bur-den, And leaves me with a song.
to the Lord be-long," Then Je-sus took my bur-den, And left me with a song.
a - ges roll a - long, How Je-sus took my bur-den, And left me with a song.
CHORUS
Yes, Je-sus took my bur-den I could no lon-ger bear, Yes, Je-sus took my
bur-den In an-swer to my prayer; My anx-ious fears sub-sid-ed My

JESUS TOOK MY BURDEN
spir-it was made strong, For Je-sus took my bur-den, And left me with a song.
52
MY JESUS, I LOVE THEE
(Second tune with chorus)
WILLIAM R. FEATHERSTONE
Chorus by A. B. S.
Netherlands Melody
1. My Je - sus, I love Thee, I know Thou art mine; For Thee all the fol-lies
2. I love Thee be-cause Thou hast first lov-ed me, And purchased my par-don
3. I'll love Thee in life, I will love Thee in death, And praise Thee as long as
4. In man-sions of glo - ry and end - less de-light, I'll ev - er a - dore Thee
of sin I re - sign; My gra - cious Re - deem - er, my Sav-iour art Thou;
on Cal - va - ry's tree; I love Thee for wear - ing the thorns on Thy brow;
Thou lendest me breath; And say when the death-dew lies cold on my brow,
in heav - en so bright; I'll sing with the glit - ter - ing crown on my brow,
If ev - er I loved Thee, my Je - sus 'tis now.
CHORUS
Je - sus, Je - sus,
Name that I love, Blest Name of my Sav - iour, Who came from a - bove.

53

OH, IT IS WONDERFUL

Mabel J. Rosemon
Grant Colfax Tullar
Duet Smoothly
1. In His un-dy-ing love, Christ came from heav'n a-bove, Came to re-
2. While we in sin were dead, Christ the Re-deem-er bled, Suf-fered and
3. Je-sus, the Ho-ly One, God's well-be-lov-ed Son, Of-fers to
rit.
deem us from death and de-spair; . . . . . Come, then, make no de-lay,
sor-rowed on Cal-va-ry's tree; . . . . . Match-less the love He showed,
ran-som thy sin-bur-dened soul; . . . . . Pleads with thee ten-der-ly,
turn from thy sin a-way, Cast-ing on Him ev-'ry sor-row and care.
it was the debt we owed, Bless-ed the tho't, that He suf-fered for me.
will-ing to par-don thee; Yield to His love, let Him make thee whole.
Chorus
Oh, it is won-der-ful, so ver-y won-der-ful, That we by
rit.
a tempo
grace should be Saved thro' e-ter-ni-ty; Oh, it is won-der-ful,

OH, IT IS WONDERFUL

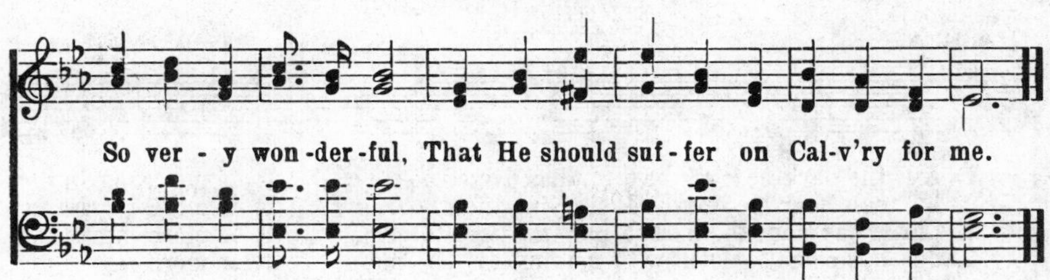
So ver - y won - der - ful, That He should suf - fer on Cal - v'ry for me.

54 ALL FOR ME

C. F. W. — C. F. WEIGLE.

Slowly.

1. Je - sus was rich; He be-came poor; Love filled His heart di - vine; All He could give, wealth ev - er - more, He gave this soul of mine.
2. Un - der the cross I stand and gaze; Was e'er such ag - o - ny? Love so di - vine fills with a - maze, Christ gave Him-self for me.
3. All that I am, all that I have Yield - ed to Christ shall be; Won by His grace, moved by His love, He shall be all to me.

CHORUS.

All for me, all for me, Je - sus in love gave all for me;
All for me, all for me, Je - sus gave all for me.

55 IT IS MORNING IN MY HEART

A. H. A. Rev. A. H. Ackley.

1. All the dark-ness of the night has passed a - way, It is morn-ing in my
2. I can hear the songbirds sing-ing their re-frain, It is morn-ing in my
3. Christ has made the world a par - a - dise to me, It is morn-ing in my
4. Joy has come to dwell with me for - ev - er - more, It is morn-ing in my
heart; I am liv-ing in the sun-light of the day, It is
heart; And I know that life for me be-gins a - gain, It is
heart; Ev-'ry du - ty in the light of love I see, It is
heart, I shall sing it when I reach the oth - er shore, It is
REFRAIN
morn-ing in my heart. It is morning, it is morning in my heart, . . .
in my heart,
Je-sus made the gloomy shadows all de - part; . . . . . Songs of gladness now I
made all de-part;
sing, for since Je-sus is my King It is morning, it is morn-ing in my heart.

GLORIOUS CALVARY

ALFRED B. SMITH
Free trans. from Swedish

Arr. by HERMAN VOSS

1. Once by the sin of the world I was bound, But Je-sus res-cued me;
2. Now I am free from the pow-er of sin, Since Je-sus set me free;
3. Come, then, to Cal-v'ry, O sin bur-dened soul, Let Je-sus set you free;
Lift-ed me up, put my feet on high ground, Glo-ri-ous Cal-va-ry.
Joy-bells are ring-ing, there's gladness with-in, Glo-ri-ous Cal-va-ry.
You, too, will join with the ran-somed made whole, Glo-ri-ous Cal-va-ry.
CHORUS
Glo-ri-ous Cal-va-ry, Glo-ri-ous Cal-va-ry, My debt there was
rit.
paid and my soul was set free, Glo-ri-ous Cal-va-ry.

57 WHEN YOU OPEN YOUR HEART'S DOOR TO JESUS

W. R. C.
W. R. Cole.
1. I have found a Com-pan - ion so pre-cious and true, He is con-stant-ly near me the whole day thro'; By His won-der-ful grace I ob-tained life a - new, When I opened my heart's door to Him.(to Him.)
2. Tho' with sor-row and care you are oft - en dis-tressed, Tho' with bur-dens of sin you are sore depressed, There is comfort and peace, there is heav-en-ly rest, When you open your heart's door to Him.(to Him.)
3. Je - sus of -fers sal - va - tion to all who be - lieve, He will save ev - 'ry one who His grace re-ceives, He will sure - ly sup-ply all your soul's earthly needs, When you open your heart's door to Him.(to Him.)
4. He is stand-ing be-fore your heart's por-tal to - day, Do not turn from His voice, nev-er-more de - lay, Trust Him now as your Saviour and fol-low His way, And open your heart's door to Him.(to Him)
CHORUS.
When you open your heart's door to Je - sus, When you open your heart's door to Him, ... your heart's door to Him, Heaven's joys o'er your soul will like sea bil-lows roll, When you o-pen your heart's door to Him.
ritard.

IT TOOK JESUS TO RESCUE ME

H. B. Herbert Buffum.

1. I was drift-ing a-lone, with no pi-lot to guide, Far a-way on life's troub-le-some sea, When it seemed that the bil-lows I could not out-ride, It took Je-sus to res-cue me.
2. How I laughed at the dan-gers of which I was told! Yes, I tho't I was hap-py and free, But I failed to break loose from the sin-chains which hold; It took Je-sus to res-cue me.
3. I was just a lost sheep wand'ring farther each day, Till the night came and I could not see; And no hu-man hand reached out to point me the way, It took Je-sus to res-cue me.
4. Now I'm safe in the life-boat and laugh at the storms, And I'm tell-ing to oth-ers how He, My great Pi-lot so true, came my lost soul to save: It took Je-sus to res-cue me.
CHORUS.
It took Je-sus to res-cue me,...... It took Jesus to res-cue me;...... When I sought for re-lease, Sought in vain for sweet peace, It took Je-sus to res-cue me.
res-cue me, res-cue me;

59 TO DO THE FATHER'S WILL

H. G.
Helen Griggs
DUET
1. It was a - lone that Je - sus suf - fered in Geth - sem - a - ne, A - lone He drained the bit - ter cup of deep - est woe for me, A - lone He bore the rug - ged cross on Cal - v'ry's dark - ened hill; The Sav - iour came to do the Fa - ther's will. . . . .
2. It was a - lone that Je - sus died up - on the cru - el tree, A - lone He shed His pre - cious blood in cleansing pow'r for me, A - lone He lay in earth's dark pris - on, si - lent, cold, and still; The Sav - iour died to do the Fa - ther's will. . . . .
3. It was a - lone that Je - sus rose from out the tight - sealed tomb, A - lone He con - quered death and scat - tered all its fear and gloom, A - lone the pur - pose of His Fa - ther He did thus ful - fill; The Sav - iour lives to do the Fa - ther's will. . . . .
4. It was a - lone that Je - sus cast my sin so far a - way, A - lone He saved my sin - ful soul from that dread judg - ment day, A - lone with peace and name - less joy He all my heart doth fill; And now I seek to do my Fa - ther's will. . . . .
CHORUS
A - lone, yes, all a - lone, the Sav - iour died for me; A - lone, yes, all a -

TO DO THE FATHER'S WILL

lone, from sin He set me free; Without a hope, this world was sunk in sin and
shame un - til The Saviour came to do the Fa - ther's will. . . .

60

THE QUIET HOUR

SPEAK, LORD, IN THE STILLNESS

E. MAY GRIMES

Arr. by
ALFRED B. SMITH

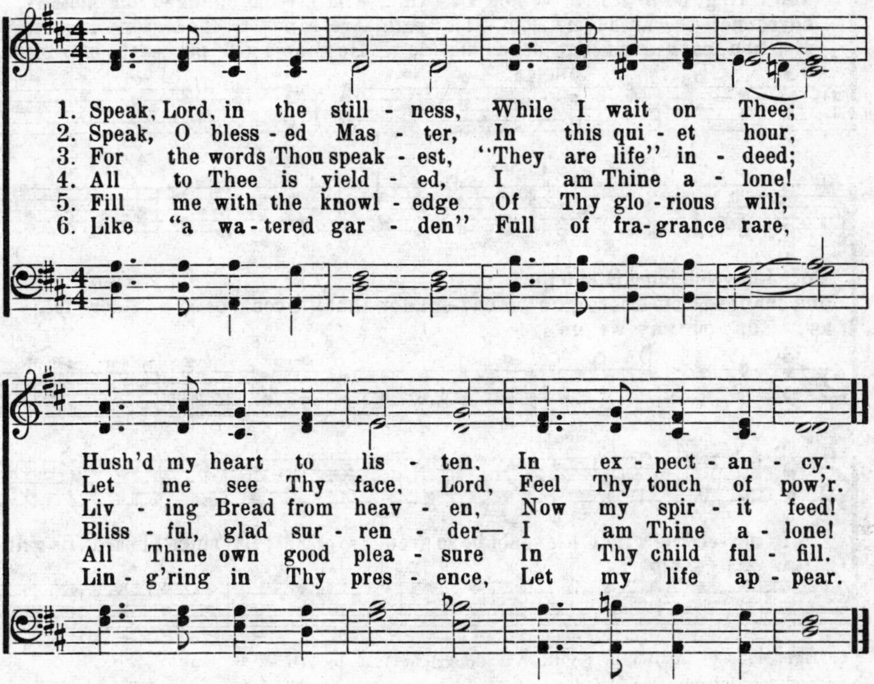

1. Speak, Lord, in the still - ness, While I wait on Thee;
2. Speak, O bless - ed Mas - ter, In this qui - et hour,
3. For the words Thou speak - est, "They are life" in - deed;
4. All to Thee is yield - ed, I am Thine a - lone!
5. Fill me with the knowl - edge Of Thy glo - rious will;
6. Like "a wa - tered gar - den" Full of fra - grance rare,

Hush'd my heart to lis - ten, In ex - pect - an - cy.
Let me see Thy face, Lord, Feel Thy touch of pow'r.
Liv - ing Bread from heav - en, Now my spir - it feed!
Bliss - ful, glad sur - ren - der— I am Thine a - lone!
All Thine own good plea - sure In Thy child ful - fill.
Lin - g'ring in Thy pres - ence, Let my life ap - pear.

61 I'VE FOUND REAL JOY

C. H. L. C. HAROLD LOWDEN

Moderato
1. Be-fore I met my Sav-iour, my heart was troub-led sore, I
2. In Him I'm ful-ly trust-ing each mo-ment of the day, With
3. I rev-el in His Pres-ence–such fel-low-ship is rare, He's
knew I was a sin-ner and doomed for-ev-er more; But one day in my
Him be-side to guide me, I nev-er lose my way; The things that once an-
with me when the storm breaks, and when the day is fair; Each joy-ous as-pir-
wan-d'ring, I heard a Voice Di-vine, And life has changed com-plete-ly,
noyed me, or caused me bit-ter pain, Are sanc-ti-fied for-ev-er
a-tion, each grief that bends me low, He shares with me each mo-ment,
CHORUS
since I have claimed Him mine.
and changed from loss to gain. I nev-er knew that life could be so won-der-ful,
as on our way we go.
I nev-er knew that life could be so grand (so grand); But since I heard His call,

I'VE FOUND REAL JOY

And yield - ed Him my all, I've found real joy and peace in trust-ing Je - sus.

62 I SHALL BE LIKE HIM

W. A. S. Rev. W. A. Spencer

1. When I shall reach the more ex-cel-lent glo-ry, And all my tri-als are passed,
2. We shall not wait till the glo - ri-ous dawning Breaks on the vi-sion so fair,
3. More and more like Him, repeat the blest story, O - ver and o - ver a -gain,

I shall be like Him, O won-der-ful sto-ry! I shall be like Him at last.
Now we may welcome the heav-en-ly morning, Now we His image may bear.
Changed by His Spirit from glo-ry to glo-ry, I shall be sat - is - fied then.

Chorus

I shall be like Him, I shall be like Him, And in His beau - ty shall shine,

I shall be like Him, wondrously like Him, Je-sus, my Sav-iour di - vine.

THE NAIL SCARRED HAND

B. B. McK. | B. B. McKinney.

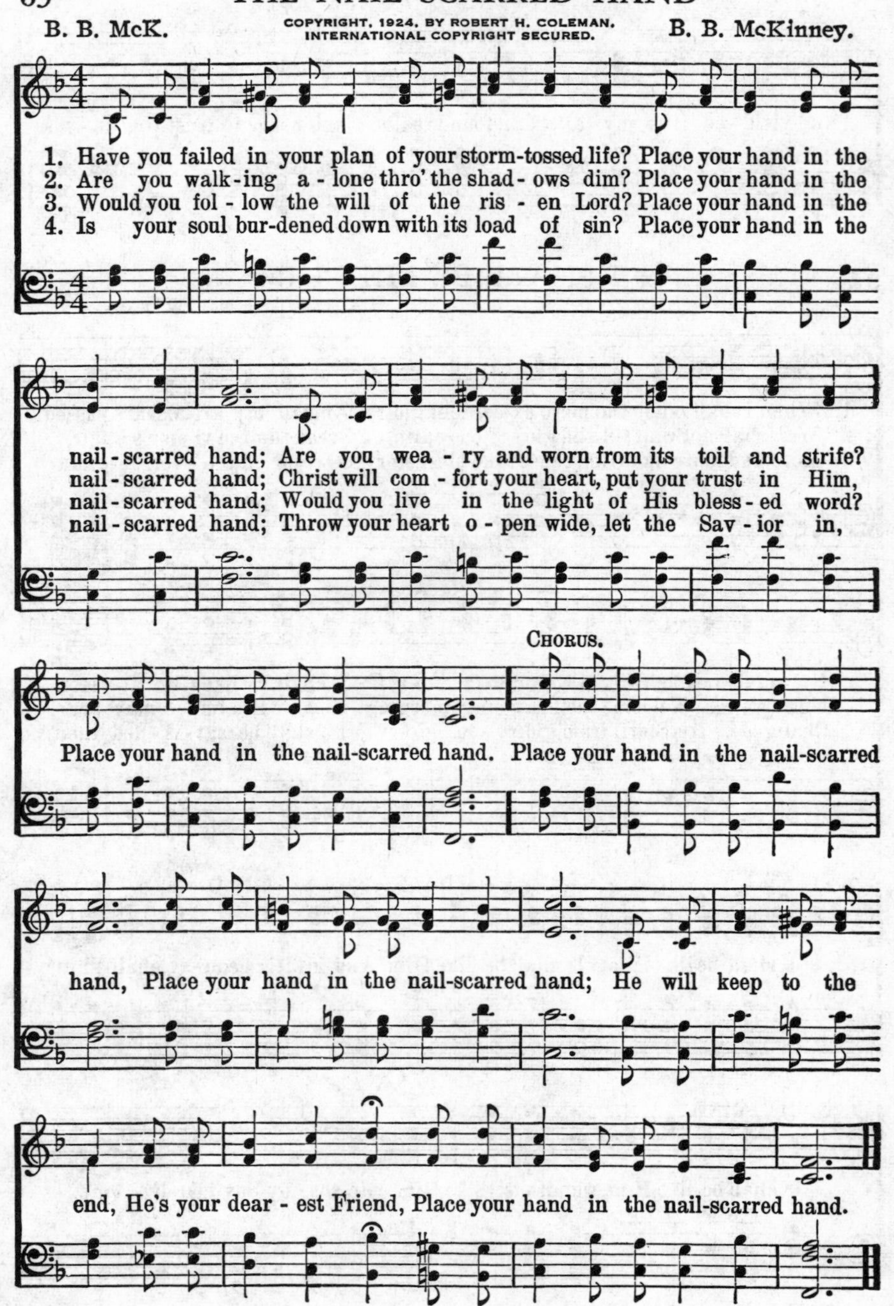
1. Have you failed in your plan of your storm-tossed life? Place your hand in the
2. Are you walk-ing a-lone thro' the shad-ows dim? Place your hand in the
3. Would you fol-low the will of the ris-en Lord? Place your hand in the
4. Is your soul bur-dened down with its load of sin? Place your hand in the
nail-scarred hand; Are you wea-ry and worn from its toil and strife?
nail-scarred hand; Christ will com-fort your heart, put your trust in Him,
nail-scarred hand; Would you live in the light of His bless-ed word?
nail-scarred hand; Throw your heart o-pen wide, let the Sav-ior in,
CHORUS.
Place your hand in the nail-scarred hand. Place your hand in the nail-scarred
hand, Place your hand in the nail-scarred hand; He will keep to the
end, He's your dear-est Friend, Place your hand in the nail-scarred hand.

THE SHEPHERD OF LOVE

A. S. R. Albert Simpson Reitz.

DUET.

1. The Shep-herd of Love is seek-ing the lost In paths that are
2. The Shep-herd of Love knows His sheep by name, And ten - der - ly
3. The Shep-herd of Love our ran - som hath paid, And of - fers sal-
4. The Shep-herd of Love now seek-eth His sheep, He seek-eth what-

rough and steep; He's call-ing the lambs that have gone a - stray,
leads the way; O wea - ry one, come to the Shepherd's fold,
va - tion free; He's pa - tient - ly wait - ing for thee to come,
e'er the cost; Be - hold, He is call - ing the wan-d'rer home,

rit. CHORUS.

He's call-ing, call-ing His sheep.
He's call - ing, call - ing to - day. Out of your dark-ness of
He's call - ing, call - ing for thee. Call - ing,
He's call - ing, call - ing the lost.

sin and shame, In - to His love, for - ev - er the same; Come to Him
call - ing, Call - ing, call - ing,

ad lib.

now, be - lieve on His name, O an - swer the call to - day.

MY ROSE OF SHARON

Warner R. Cole. W. R. Cole.

Slowly.
1. There is One all un - seen I cher - ish, Ev - er loy - al, ten - der,
2. When the tri - als of life o'er-take me, And I'm tempt-ed to go a-
3. Won't you turn to this Friend and Sav-iour? Why not yield to His love to-
true; With a won - der - ful love He cares for me; Let me
stray, 'Tis the bright Morn - ing Star that guides me back To the
day? Let His blood cleanse you from all sin and guilt, And....
sing of this Friend to you.
up - ward and homeward way.
wipe ev - 'ry tear a - way.
CHORUS.
For the Rose of Shar-on is pre - cious to
ritard
me, And the Lil - y of the Val - ley blooms in my heart e - ter - nal-
ly. Of ten thou-sand He's the fair - est, Rock of A - ges, cleft for

MY ROSE OF SHARON

me; Let me live my life for Je - sus Till His face I see.

66 MY HOME, SWEET HOME

N. B. V. | N. B. Vandall.

Legato.

1. Walk-ing a-long life's road one day, I heard a voice so sweet-ly say, "A place up in heav'n I am building thee, A beau-ti-ful, beau-ti-ful home."
2. Loved ones up-on that shore I'll meet, Casting their crowns at Jesus' feet; I'll worship and praise Him for-ev-er-more, In my beau-ti-ful, beau-ti-ful home.
3. Life's day is short, I soon shall go, To be with Him who loved me so.—I see in the distance that shining shore, My beau-ti-ful, beau-ti-ful home.

CHORUS. *p* ... *f* ... *ff*

Home, sweet home, home, sweet home, Where I'll nev-er roam;......
I see the light of that cit-y so bright, My home, sweet home.

67 TEACH ME TO PRAY

Albert Simpson Reitz — Albert Simpson Reitz

SOLO
1. Teach me to pray, Lord, teach me to pray; This is my
2. Pow - er in prayer, Lord, pow - er in prayer, Here 'mid earth's
3. My weak-ened will, Lord, Thou canst re - new; My sin - ful
4. Teach me to pray, Lord, teach me to pray; Thou art my
heart-cry, day un-to day; I long to know Thy will and Thy way;
sin and sor-row and care; Men lost and dy - ing, souls in de - spair:
na - ture Thou canst sub-due; Fill me just now with pow-er a - new:
Pat - tern, day un-to day; Thou art my Sure - ty, now and for aye;
Teach me to pray, Lord, teach me to pray.
O give me pow - er, pow-er in prayer!
Pow - er to pray, and pow-er to do!
Teach me to pray, Lord, teach me to pray.
CHORUS
Liv-ing in Thee, Lord,
and Thou in me; Con-stant a-bid-ing, this is my plea; Grant me Thy
pow - er, boundless and free: Pow-er with men and pow-er with Thee.

NOTHING BUT LEAVES

Mrs. H. S. L.
Mrs. H. S. Lehman.
1. The Mas - ter is seek-ing a har - vest In lives He's re-deemed by His blood; He seeks for the fruit of the Spir - it, And works that will glo-ri-fy God.
2. He looks for His like-ness re-flect - ed In lives that are yield-ed and true; He's look - ing for zeal in the win - ning Of souls He's en-trust-ed to you.
3. He's yearn-ing for some-one to car - - ry The life - giv-ing word far and near; He's wait - ing for hearts that are will - ing, For ears that are o-pen to hear.
CHORUS.
Nothing but leaves for the Mas - ter, Oh, how His lov-ing heart grieves, When in-stead of the fruit He is seek - ing, We of-fer Him noth-ing but leaves.

LONG AGO

Maude Wilson. Robert Harkness.

1. My soul was heav - y - la - den and wea - ry seemed the way, With
2. I came and found my Sav-iour, with arm out-stretched in love He
3. There is no friend like Je - sus to bind the bro - ken heart, I've
care and sin my heart was sore oppressed; But Je - sus bade me lis - ten— I
raised me up and told me to be glad; He showed me that the heav-ens are
tried Him and I know Him to be true; He fills me with His glad-ness, He
heard Him soft - ly say, "Come un - to Me, poor sin - ner, and have rest."
ev - er bright a - bove, That none of His dear chil-dren need be sad.
heal - eth ev - 'ry smart, O why not let Him be your Sav - iour too?
CHORUS. R. H.
I left it all with Je - sus long a - go, I left it all with
Je - sus long a - go: My ev - 'ry care and sor - row, The

LONG AGO
bur-den of to-mor-row, I left it all with Je-sus long a-go.
70
YIELDED
C. F. Warren.
Robert Harkness.
1. Low-ly and humbly, Lord, here I bow, Con-trite and broken, help me just now;
2. At Thy blest feet, Lord, teach me, I pray, Guide ev-'ry step, Lord, all thro' this day;
3. Keep ev'ry tho't, Lord, in Thy con-trol, Let Thine own presence now fill my soul;
4. Read-y and will-ing Thee to o-bey, Si-lent, if need be, have Thine own way;
Patient and still, Lord, O let me be Fit-ted for service, cleansed, Lord, by Thee.
Safe in Thy keep-ing, ev-er se-cure, Send from a-bove, Lord, strength to en-dure.
Self on the al-tar, yield-ed to Thee, Je-sus, my Sav-iour, faith-ful to be.
In full sub-mis-sion all do I give, Nothing with-hold, Lord, in me now live.
CHORUS.
Yield-ed, Lord, to Thee, Yield-ed, Lord, to Thee; Whol-ly
yield-ed, yield-ed;
p
pp
Thine, for-ev-er-more, Yield-ed, yield-ed, yield-ed, Lord, to Thee.

71

WHEN WE SEE CHRIST

E.K.R. Esther Kerr Rusthoi

1. Oft times the day seems long, our tri - als hard to bear; We're
2. Some times the sky looks dark, with not a ray of light; We're
3. Life's day will soon be o'er, all storms for - ev - er past; We'll
tempt - ed to com - plain, To mur - mur and de - spair; But
tossed and driv - en on, No hu - man help in sight; But
cross the great di - vide To glo - ry, safe at last; We'll
Christ will soon ap - pear, To catch His Bride a - way, All
there is one in heav'n, Who knows our deep - est care, Let
share the joys of heav'n, A harp, a home, a crown; The
tears for - ev - er o - ver, In God's e - ter - nal day.
Je - sus solve your prob - lem, Just go to Him in pray'r.
tempt - er will be ban - ished, We'll lay our bur - den down.
CHORUS
It will be worth it all, When we see Je - sus; Life's trials will

WHEN WE SEE CHRIST

seem so small,— when we see Christ;— One glimpse of His dear face,— All sor-row
will e-rase,— so brave-ly run the race,— Till we see Christ.

72 I'M IN HIS CARE

(Ev'ry Moment, Night and Day)

Inscribed to Trinity Baptist Church, Pasadena, Calif.

W. P. L. Wendell P. Loveless

I'm in His care, I'm in His keep-ing ev-'ry mo-ment, night and day; I'm

and day;

in His care A-wake or sleep-ing, Ev-'ry mo-ment, night and day; For

I am His, His love en-cir-cles me, And He will keep thru all e-ter-ni-ty For I am

in His care, I'm in His keep-ing, Ev-'ry mo-ment, night and day.

73 THE SAVIOR FOR ME

W. M. R. William M. Runyan

DUET

1. From heav - en a - bove, in His in - fi - nite love, Came Je - sus, a Sav - ior to be; And He scorned the deep pain our ran - som to gain,
2. The birds had their nest and the peo - ple their rest, While Je - sus all night made His plea; On the moun-tain a - lone was the Fa-ther's dear Son,
3. For sil - ver be-trayed, in mock pur - ple ar - rayed, Con-demned to a death on the tree; Then they led Him a - way on that Won-der-ful Day,

O He is the Sav - ior for me. . . . . .
the Sav - ior for me.

CHORUS

O Je - sus is will - ing to be . . . . . A Sav - ior for sin - ners like me, . . . And the bur - den will roll From the
and wait - ing to be
e - ven me,

THE SAVIOR FOR ME

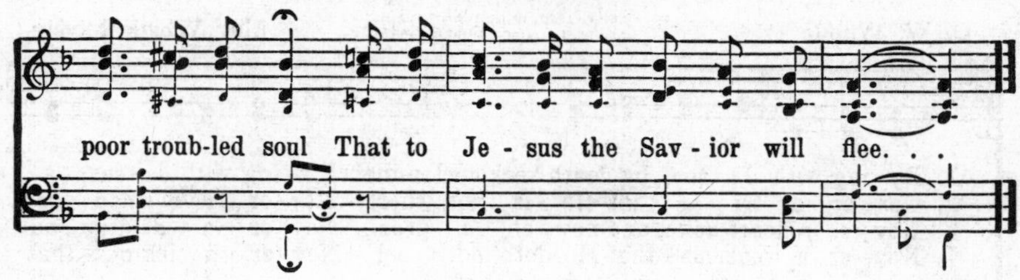
poor troub-led soul That to Je - sus the Sav - ior will flee. . .

74 I WANT YOU TO KNOW HIM

W. M. Lighthall and C. H. G. Chas. H. Gabriel.

1. I have a Sav - ior I want you to know, One to whom close - ly I cling;
One who is with me wher-ev - er I go, Je - sus, my Lord and my King.

2. I was a cap - tive—my ran - som he paid, Made me an heir to his throne;
Now I re - joice, and am nev - er a - fraid, He will not leave me a - lone.

3. Will you not meet him, this Je - sus of mine? Why not in him be made whole?
What shall it prof - it with all the world thine, Gained by the loss of thy soul?

4. Come to the cross of my cru - ci - fied Lord, Learn of his pow - er to save;
There let the sins of thy heart be out-poured, There claim the promise he gave.

5. Then in my Sav - ior a Friend you will find Who can for - give-ness be - stow;
When to him all you have full - y re - signed, Then you will love him, I know.

CHORUS.

I want you to know him, I want you to own him, I want you to love (love) him, too;
I want you to know him; To know is to love him; I want you to love my King.

75 MOMENT BY MOMENT

D. W. Whittle
COPYRIGHT, 1920, BY MAY WHITTLE MOODY
RENEWAL. USED BY PERMISSION
May Whittle Moody
1. Dy-ing with Je-sus, by death reckoned mine; Liv-ing with Je-sus, a
2. Nev-er a tri-al that He is not there, Nev-er a bur-den that
3. Nev-er a heart-ache, and nev-er a groan, Nev-er a tear-drop and
4. Nev-er a weak-ness that He doth not feel, Nev-er a sick-ness that
new life di-vine; Look-ing to Je-sus till glo-ry doth shine, Mo-ment by
He doth not bear, Nev-er a sor-row that He doth not share, Mo-ment by
nev-er a moan; Nev-er a dan-ger but there on the throne, Mo-ment by
He can-not heal; Mo-ment by mo-ment, in woe or in weal, Je-sus, my
mo-ment, O Lord, I am Thine.
mo-ment, I'm un-der His care. Mo-ment by mo-ment I'm kept in His love;
mo-ment He thinks of His own.
Sav-iour, a-bides with me still.
Mo-ment by mo-ment I've life from a-bove; Look-ing to Je-sus till
glo-ry doth shine; Mo-ment by mo-ment, O Lord, I am Thine.

A PASSION FOR SOULS

HERBERT G. TOVEY
FOSS L. FELLERS
1. Give me a pas - sion for souls, dear Lord, A pas - sion to save the lost;
2. Though there are dan-gers un-told and stern Con-front-ing me in the way,
3. How shall this pas - sion for souls be mine? Lord, make Thou the an-swer clear;
O that Thy love were by all a-dored, And wel-comed at an - y cost.
Will-ing-ly still would I go, nor turn, But trust Thee for grace each day.
Help me to throw out the old Life-Line To those who are strug-gling near.
CHORUS.
Je - sus, I long, I long to be win-ning Men who are
lost, and con - stant - ly sin - ning; O may this hour be
one of be - gin - ning The sto - ry of par - don to tell.

77 LEAD ME GENTLY HOME, FATHER

W. L. T.
W. L. Thompson.
1. Lead me gen-tly home, Fa-ther, Lead me gen-tly home, When life's toils are
2. Lead me gen-tly home, Fa-ther, Lead me gen-tly home, In life's dark-est
end - ed, And part-ing days have come; Sin no more shall tempt me, Ne'er from
hours, Father, When life's troubles come; Keep my feet from wand'ring, Lest from
Thee I'll roam, If Thou'lt on - ly lead me, Fa-ther, Lead me gen-tly home.
Thee I'll roam, Lest I fall up-on the way-side, Lead me gen-tly home.
rit.
p
CHORUS.
Lead me gen - tly home, Fa - ther, lead me gen - tly
Lead me gen - tly home, Fa - ther, Lead me gen - tly home, Fa - ther,

LEAD ME GENTLY HOME, FATHER

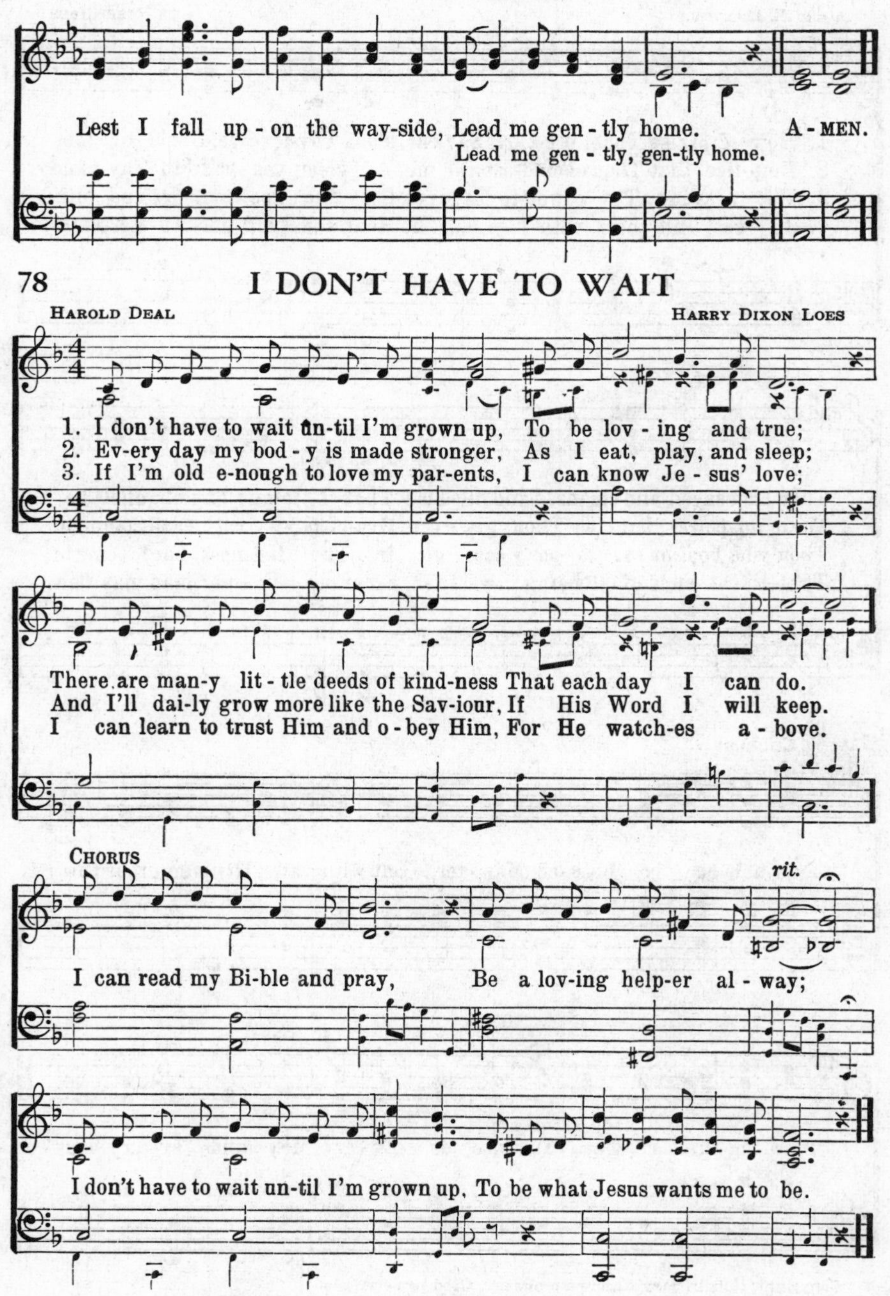
Lest I fall up - on the way-side, Lead me gen - tly home. A - MEN.
Lead me gen - tly, gen - tly home.
78 I DON'T HAVE TO WAIT
HAROLD DEAL
HARRY DIXON LOES
1. I don't have to wait un-til I'm grown up, To be lov - ing and true;
2. Ev-ery day my bod - y is made stronger, As I eat, play, and sleep;
3. If I'm old e-nough to love my par-ents, I can know Je - sus' love;
There are man-y lit - tle deeds of kind-ness That each day I can do.
And I'll dai-ly grow more like the Sav-iour, If His Word I will keep.
I can learn to trust Him and o - bey Him, For He watch-es a - bove.
CHORUS
rit.
I can read my Bi-ble and pray, Be a lov-ing help-er al - way;
I don't have to wait un-til I'm grown up, To be what Jesus wants me to be.

CHANNELS ONLY

Mary E. Maxwell — Ada Rose Gibbs

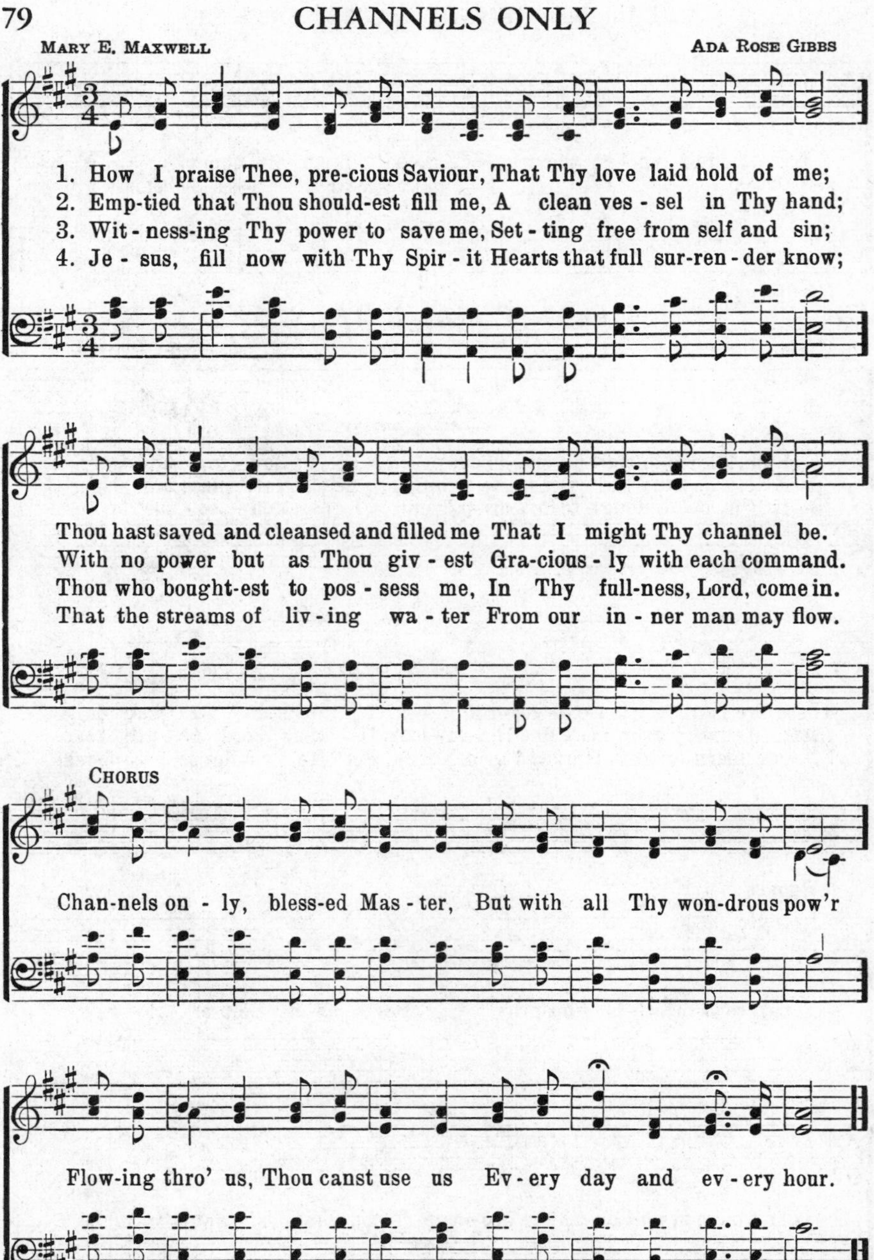
1. How I praise Thee, pre-cious Saviour, That Thy love laid hold of me;
2. Emp-tied that Thou should-est fill me, A clean ves - sel in Thy hand;
3. Wit - ness-ing Thy power to save me, Set - ting free from self and sin;
4. Je - sus, fill now with Thy Spir - it Hearts that full sur-ren - der know;
Thou hast saved and cleansed and filled me That I might Thy channel be.
With no power but as Thou giv - est Gra-cious - ly with each command.
Thou who bought-est to pos - sess me, In Thy full-ness, Lord, come in.
That the streams of liv - ing wa - ter From our in - ner man may flow.
CHORUS
Chan-nels on - ly, bless-ed Mas - ter, But with all Thy won-drous pow'r
Flow-ing thro' us, Thou canst use us Ev - ery day and ev - ery hour.

JESUS LEADS

JOHN R. CLEMENTS

JNO. R. SWENEY

Andante
1. Like a shep-herd, ten-der, true, Je-sus leads,... Je-sus leads,...
2. All a-long life's rug-ged road Je-sus leads,... Je-sus leads,...
3. Thro' the sun-lit ways of life Je-sus leads,... Je-sus leads,...
Je-sus leads, Je-sus leads,
Dai-ly finds us pas-tures new, Je-sus leads,... Je-sus leads;
Till we reach yon blest a-bode, Je-sus leads,... Je-sus leads;
Thro' the warrings and the strife Je-sus leads,... Je-sus leads;
Je-sus leads, Je-sus leads;
If thick mists are o'er the way, Or the flock 'mid danger feeds,
All the way, be-fore, He's trod, And He now the flock precedes,
When we reach the Jordan's tide, Where life's bound'ry-line re-cedes,
If thick mists are o'er the way, Or the flock 'mid danger feeds,
rit.
He will watch them lest they stray, Je-sus leads,... Je-sus leads.
Safe in-to the fold of God, Je-sus leads,... Je-sus leads.
He will spread the waves a-side, Je-sus leads,... Je-sus leads.
Je-sus leads,

81

BY LIFE, OR BY DEATH*

PHIL. 1: 20

© COPYRIGHT, 1938, RENEWAL, 1966
THE RODEHEAVER CO., OWNER
INTERNATIONAL COPYRIGHT SECURED
WILL H. HOUGHTON
GEORGE S. SCHULER
1. So this is life, this world with all its pleasures, Struggles and tears, a smile, a
2. In life or death—and life is sure-ly fly - ing, The crib and coffin carved from the
3. Help me to know the val - ue of these hours, Help me the fol - ly of all
rit.
frown, a sigh, Friendship so true, and love of kin and neighbor? Sometimes 'tis
self - same tree. In life or death—and death so soon is com-ing—Es-cape I
waste to see; Help me to trust the Christ who bore my sorrows, And thus to
rit.
hard to live—al-ways, to die! The world moves on, so rap - id - ly the
can - not, there's no place to flee— But Thou, O God, hast life that is e-
yield for life or death to Thee. In all my days be glo - ri - fied, Lord
liv - ing The forms of those who dis-ap-pear re - place, And each one dreams that
ter - nal; That life is mine, a gift thro' Thy dear Son. Help me to feel its
Je - sus, In all my ways guide me with Thine own eye; Just when and as Thou
ad lib.
he will be en - dur - ing—How soon that one be-comes the miss ing face!
flush and pulse su-per - nal, As - sur-ance of the morn when life is done.
wilt, use me, Lord Je - sus, And then for me 'tis Christ, to live or die.

*In loving memory of John and Betty Stam, martyred in China, December 8, 1934

82 WHY DO I SING ABOUT JESUS?

COPYRIGHT, 1923, BY HARRY D. CLARKE
A. A. K.
Albert Allen Ketchum
1. Deep in my heart there's a glad - ness, Je - sus has saved me from sin!
2. On - ly a glimpse of His good - ness, That was suf - fi-cient for me;
3. He is the fair - est of fair ones, He is the Lil - y, the Rose;
Praise to His name—what a Sav - iour! Cleansing with-out and with-in.
On - ly one look at the Sav - iour, Then was my spir - it set free.
Riv - ers of mer - cy sur-round Him, Grace, love and pit - y He shows.
CHORUS Unison
Why do I sing a - bout Je - - - sus? Why is He
pre - cious to me? . . . . He is my Lord and my
Sav - - iour,— Dy - ing! He set me free! . . . .

I'VE HAD A GLIMPSE OF JESUS

John R. Clements. Elisha A. Hoffman.

DUET. Sop. and Alto
1. Back to the cold world I will not go, Back to the old paths of
2. Back on the night shrouded sea to die? Back where the break-ers of
3. Back to the boon friends of for-mer days, Still walk-ing on in their
pain and of woe, Back to the old life of sin, O no! I've had a
sin toss on high? Back, 'mid the bil-lows of doubt? Not I! I've had a
old, sin-ful ways? Back with a mes-sage of love and grace; I've had a
DUET.. Sop. and Alto.
glimpse of Je-sus. I've found a life that is sweet-er to me,
Sweet-er with peace, from un-hap-pi-ness free, Full-er of joy than the
CHORUS.
old life could be; I've had a glimpse of Je-sus.
Back to the cold world I
Back to the old life of

I'VE HAD A GLIMPSE OF JESUS

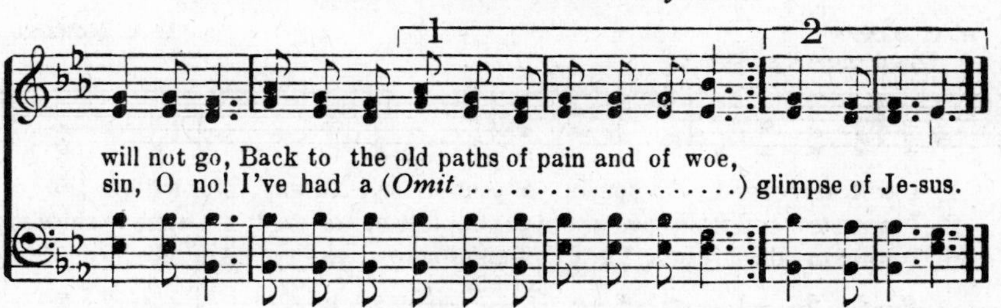
1
2
will not go, Back to the old paths of pain and of woe,
sin, O no! I've had a (Omit.....................) glimpse of Je-sus.

84 HAVE YOU ANY ROOM FOR JESUS?

Arr. by W. W. D. from L. W. M. — C. C. WILLIAMS

1. Have you an - y room for Je - sus, He who bore your load of sin;
2. Room for pleasure, room for busi-ness, But for Christ the cru - ci - fied,
3. Have you an - y room for Je - sus, As in grace He calls a - gain?
4. Room and time now give to Je - sus, Soon will pass God's day of grace;

As He knocks and asks ad-mis - sion, Sin - ner, will you let Him in?
Not a place that He can en - ter, In the heart for which He died?
O to - day is time ac-cept - ed, To-mor - row you may call in vain.
Soon thy heart left cold and si - lent, And Thy Sav-iour's pleading cease.

CHORUS

Room for Je - sus, King of glo - ry! Has - ten now His word o - bey;
Swing the heart's door wide-ly o - pen, Bid Him en - ter while you may.

85 MY VERY BEST FOR JESUS

W. C. MARTIN
M. L. McPHAIL
Quick march movement
1. I will not serve my Sav-ior in a poor or self-ish way, Nor with a life of
2. I w ınt to stand for Je-sus where His name is not revered; I want to show my
3. I want to do my best, for I re-mem-ber Cal-va - ry, And all the deeds of
i - dle-ness His ten-der love re - pay. I want to do the ut-most for His
col-ors where the Fa-ther is not feared; I would dis-play His glo - ry where the
ten-der love my Sav-ior did for me: I see with weeping eyes His dy - ing
glo - ry that I may— I want to do my ver - y best for Je - sus.
light hath not ap-peared—I want to do my ver - y best for Je - sus.
form up - on the tree— O, I would do my vei - y best for Je - sus.
CHORUS
My ver - y best for Je-sus is the least that I can do; And in - to serv-ice
there must go my steadfast love and true;.. And all that I can ren-der is not

MY VERY BEST FOR JESUS
half that is His due— I want to do my ver-y best for Je-sus.
86
GOD IS LOVE
GERTRUDE R. DUGAN
GEORGE S. SCHULER
1. God is love—and like the tide Flows His mer-cy deep and wide;
2. God is love—I will not fear, For He says, "Be of good cheer."
3. God is love—He giv-eth peace; Strife shall end and tu-mult cease.
And His grace tow'rd you and me Is as bound-less as the sea.
He will give me what is best, So in Him my heart shall rest.
God who do-eth all things well Will thy doubts and fears dispel.
On the clouds, so dark a-bove, Shines the rainbow of His love (His love).
rit.
Praise His name with heart and voice, God is love—let earth re-joice.
Look-ing up I see and know God is love, in weal or woe.
He will all His good-ness prove, Hal-le-lu-jah! God is love.
rit.

87 THE LIGHTHOUSE ON THE SHORE

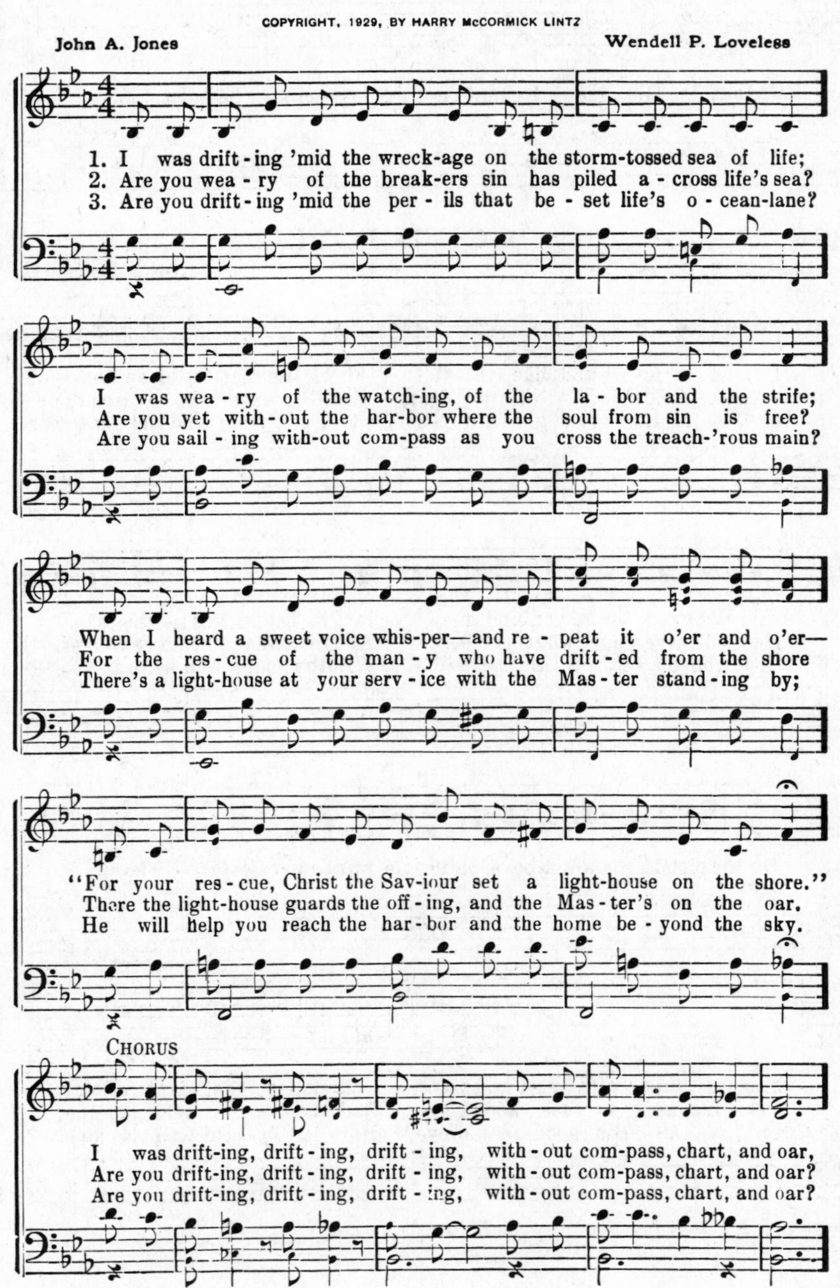
COPYRIGHT, 1929, BY HARRY McCORMICK LINTZ
John A. Jones
Wendell P. Loveless
1. I was drift-ing 'mid the wreck-age on the storm-tossed sea of life;
2. Are you wea-ry of the break-ers sin has piled a-cross life's sea?
3. Are you drift-ing 'mid the per-ils that be-set life's o-cean-lane?
I was wea-ry of the watch-ing, of the la-bor and the strife;
Are you yet with-out the har-bor where the soul from sin is free?
Are you sail-ing with-out com-pass as you cross the treach-'rous main?
When I heard a sweet voice whis-per—and re-peat it o'er and o'er—
For the res-cue of the man-y who have drift-ed from the shore
There's a light-house at your serv-ice with the Mas-ter stand-ing by;
"For your res-cue, Christ the Sav-iour set a light-house on the shore."
There the light-house guards the off-ing, and the Mas-ter's on the oar.
He will help you reach the har-bor and the home be-yond the sky.
CHORUS
I was drift-ing, drift-ing, drift-ing, with-out com-pass, chart, and oar,
Are you drift-ing, drift-ing, drift-ing, with-out com-pass, chart, and oar?
Are you drift-ing, drift-ing, drift-ing, with-out com-pass, chart, and oar?

THE LIGHTHOUSE ON THE SHORE

But was res-cued by the Mas-ter of the lighthouse on the shore....
Then I pray you call the Mas-ter of the lighthouse on the shore....
Then I pray you call the Mas-ter of the lighthouse on the shore....

88 TO DO THY WILL

W. H. Pike — Mrs. W. H. Pike

1. O gracious God, on Thee I wait, With Thine own self my be-ing fill;
2. In tri-als oft I find myself, With soul oppressed and bod-y ill;
3. And when the glimpse of glo-ry comes, That gives my soul a hap-py thrill,

As day by day my life I live, To do Thy will, Thy blessed will.
There is a place where peace is found, 'Tis in Thy will, Thy ho-ly will.
My soul shall an-swer with de-light, "I love, dear Lord, to do Thy will."

CHORUS
To do Thy will, yes, that is all; To do Thy will, o-bey Thy call;
To fol-low, Lord, where Thou dost lead, To do Thy will is all I need.

89 JESUS FILLS MY LIFE WITH PEACE AND JOY

AVIS B. CHRISTIANSEN WENDELL P. LOVELESS

Solo or Duet in verse
1. In the midst of tur-moil I have peace with-in, In the midst of sor-row, joy di-
2. In His constant keeping I have naught to fear, His sweet will is now my sole de-
3. I have found in Him a constant fount of joy, I have found in Him e - ter-nal
vine (joy di-vine); On the cross my Sav-ior bore my ev - 'ry sin, And
light (sole de-light); Glo - ry thrills my be - ing as His voice I hear—His
rest (per-fect rest); Storms my soul may threaten, but can ne'er de - stroy; In
CHORUS Parts
dwells with-in this heart of mine (of mine).
presence cheers the darkest night (dark night). Je - sus fills my life with peace and joy,
Him I am for-ev - er blest (yes, blest).
Praise His ho - ly name, He's al-ways just the same; He calms each storm that would my
faith de - stroy, Je - sus fills my life with peace and joy (peace and joy).

ONLY BELIEVE AND LIVE

R. H. | ROBERT HARKNESS

SOLO
1. Lift up your eyes to Cal-va-ry, On-ly be-lieve and live;
2. Great is God's love in Him re-vealed, On-ly be-lieve and live;
3. Naught can you do His love to win, On-ly be-lieve and live;
On yon-der cross your Sav-ior see— On-ly be-lieve and live.
Ful-ly your par-don has been sealed, On-ly be-lieve and live.
O-pen your heart and let Him in, On-ly be-lieve and live.
It was for you He bled and died, On that dread cross was cru-ci-fied,
Seek now for-give-ness full and free, Par-don and peace and lib-er-ty,
Works cannot save your trou-bled soul, On-ly His blood can make you whole,
He suf-fered sore, Your sins He bore— On-ly be-lieve and live.
Come to Him now, Be-fore Him bow, On-ly be-lieve and live.
Sim-ply ac-cept, No more re-ject, On-ly be-lieve and live.

91 IF I GAINED THE WORLD

Anna Ölander
Tr. Composite

Swedish

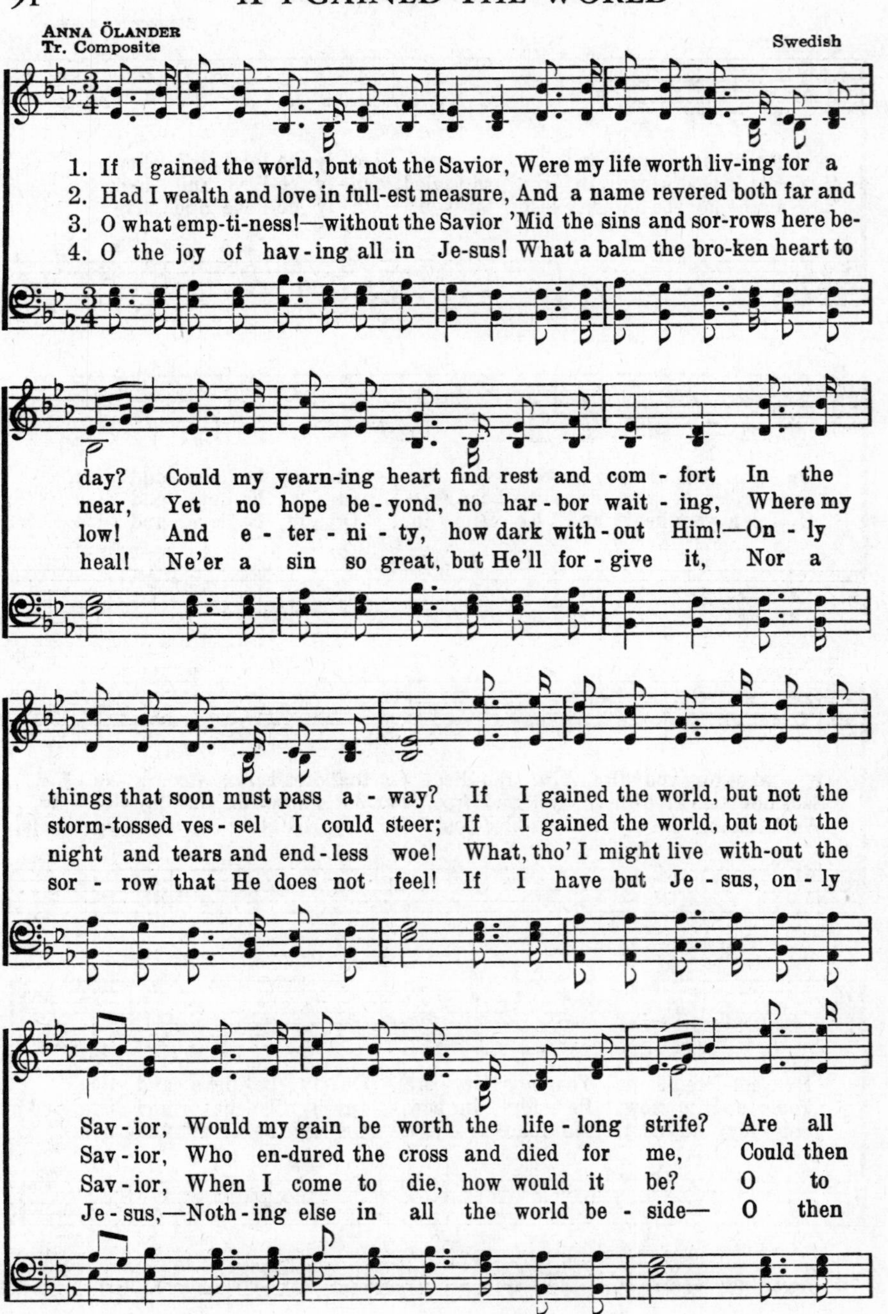
1. If I gained the world, but not the Savior, Were my life worth liv-ing for a day? Could my yearn-ing heart find rest and com - fort In the things that soon must pass a - way? If I gained the world, but not the Sav - ior, Would my gain be worth the life - long strife? Are all
2. Had I wealth and love in full-est measure, And a name revered both far and near, Yet no hope be - yond, no har - bor wait - ing, Where my storm-tossed ves - sel I could steer; If I gained the world, but not the Sav - ior, Who en-dured the cross and died for me, Could then
3. O what emp-ti-ness!—without the Savior 'Mid the sins and sor-rows here be-low! And e - ter - ni - ty, how dark with - out Him!—On - ly night and tears and end - less woe! What, tho' I might live with-out the Sav - ior, When I come to die, how would it be? O to
4. O the joy of hav-ing all in Je-sus! What a balm the bro-ken heart to heal! Ne'er a sin so great, but He'll for - give it, Nor a sor - row that He does not feel! If I have but Je - sus, on - ly Je - sus,—Noth - ing else in all the world be - side— O then

IF I GAINED THE WORLD
earth-ly pleasures worth com-par-ing For a mo-ment with a Christ-filled life?
all the world af-ford a ref - uge, Whither, in my an-guish, I might flee?
face the val-ley's gloom with-out Him! And without Him all e - ter - ni - ty!
ev - 'ry - thing is mine in Je - sus; For my needs and more He will pro-vide.
92 THOU WILT KEEP HIM IN PERFECT PEACE
V. K. A.
Isaiah 26: 3
VIVIAN KRETZ AMSLER
Thou wilt keep him in per - fect peace, whose mind is stayed on Thee;
When the shad-ows come and dark-ness falls, He giv - eth in-ward peace; Oh, He
is the on - ly per - fect rest - ing place. He giv - eth per - fect peace;.
Thou wilt keep him in per - fect peace, whose mind is stayed on Thee.

93 HE WILL NEVER CAST YOU OUT

W. R. C. W. R. Cole.

Legato.
1. When by sin and shame your hopes of life are shat - tered, And your
2. When the en - e - my at - tacks with e - vil taunt - ing, And he
3. When by grace di - vine your earth - ly walk is end - ed, And in
heart by fear is fraught with - in, with - out, Let your wea - ry soul to
casts a - cross your path the shades of doubt, With your faith in God your
glo - ry - land you join the vic - tor's shout, You will reign with Him who
Je - sus' fold be gath - ered, And re - mem - ber He will nev - er cast you
step may be un - daunt - ed, For you know that He will nev - er cast you
has your soul be - friend - ed, And you'll know that He will nev - er cast you
Chorus.
out. He will nev - er cast you out, He will
nev - er cast you out. cast you out,
Ritard.
nev - er cast you out; Trust in His e - ter - nal plan, Rest in
cast you out;

HE WILL NEVER CAST YOU OUT

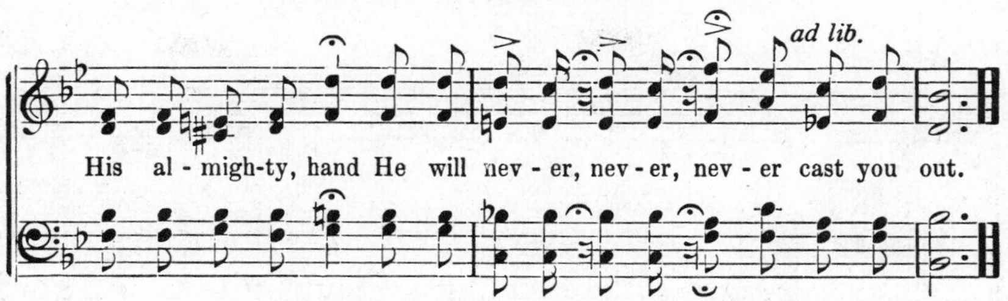
ad lib.
His al - migh-ty, hand He will nev - er, nev - er, nev - er cast you out.

94 I AM SATISFIED WITH JESUS

W. R. Cole. W. R. Cole.
Chorus by G. H. Rosenvold.

Not too fast.

1. Long I sought for peace and com-fort, In a world of sin and woe,
Till I heard the voice of Je - sus Call - ing me in ac - cents low.

2. Charms of earth can nev-er lure me From my Saviour's side a - way;
He who with His blood has bought me Sat - is - fies me day by day.

3. With His love now shin-ing thro' me I a wit - ness true will be,
Tell - ing ev - 'ry-where that Je - sus Sat - is - fies e - ter - nal - ly.

CHORUS.

I am sat - is - fied with Je - sus, I am sat - is - fied with Him;
Ev-er keeps me singing, Keeps the joy-bells ringing, I am sat-is-fied with Him.
rit.

95 YES, THERE IS COMFORT

KALEB JOHNSON
SVEN AHLVÉN
1. Is there no com - fort for sor - row, Noth - ing but heartaches and tears?
2. Is there no cure for our troub - les, Noth - ing but fail - ure and loss?
3. Must we con - tin - ual - ly stum - ble? Will noth - ing pre - cious re - main?
Is there no sun - shine to - mor - row, Noth - ing but dark - ness and fears?
Are they, our pleas - ures, but bub - bles? Are all our treas - ures but dross?
Is all we built meant to crum - ble? Are all our ef - forts in vain?
REFRAIN
Yes, there is com - fort for sor - row, There's
ten.
rest for the wea - ri - est heart.— And, praise God, there'll be sun - rise to -
ten.
mor - row; He'll re - turn, and He'll nev - er de - part.

RAINBOW LITHOGRAPHING CO.
MUSIC PRINTERS - CHICAGO, ILL.